IF I MAKE MY BED IN HELL

# IF I MAKE MY
# BED IN HELL

by
**John B. Porter**

**WORD BOOKS,** Publishers
**Waco, Texas — London, England**

In a base camp just outside Bein Hoa is a dusty road called "Bowen Street." It was named in honor of Specialist Fourth Class Ray Bowen from Hannibal, New York. Ray served as my enlisted assistant. He was a good soldier and a good friend. He was the kind of boy I would like for my daughter to marry. He never squeezed a trigger in combat, never killed, never even hated. Yet he is dead. Ray begged to go with me into combat, and he pleaded for us to stay where the action was so that we might be of help to the men in case of trouble. Trouble came, and side-by-side we lay in the midst of it. I looked into his eyes and saw faith and courage. When I looked back, his eyes were closed, not to open again. He died in my arms. I am now back home again. Two years have passed, but I still remember Ray Bowen. I would like to dedicate this book in honor of Ray and the men like him in the 173rd Airborne Brigade with whom I had the privilege of serving. In them I saw the American ideal, and in the process I became a better American. They gave the words, "duty," "honor," and "country" a new meaning. I salute their heroism, their courage, and their faith.

# Contents

1. "Raise Hell"  1

2. Riding the "Point"  13

3. They're Out There Somewhere  19

4. Watch Out for the New Guys  39

5. Have You Taken Any Scalps Yet?  51

6. Listen to My Sermon, Chappie  63

7. "You Ain't Lived Till You Tried It Once"  78

8. Stay Out of Here, Little Nigger  90

9. A Real Cool Character  101

10. Sin City  110

11. Americans Don't Eat People  128

12. I Cried Like a Baby  142

13. Angels Come in Black  154

# FOREWORD

The events related in this story are true. Since the situations, however, are of a very personal nature, I have taken the liberty to change names, dates, and places and to treat the circumstances in such a manner as to protect the individuals involved from possible detection or from comparison with the principal characters in the book. Ray Bowen, to whom this book is dedicated, is not to be confused with the Chaplain's Assistant portrayed in the story. The book is called a novel so that the true story may be told without fear of responsibility being fixed as to the reporting of any event or portrayal of any character.

# ACKNOWLEDGMENTS

I wish to express my indebtedness to several persons without whose help this book would probably not have been born. My wife, Patricia, and daughter, Sheree, were the real heroes as they carried on during my year in Viet Nam without a husband and father. When I returned, it was their encouragement that motivated my beginning the book and their understanding that allowed me to be absent from the family circle during the months required to write the story.

Mrs. Helen Davis Brown of Starke, Florida, also deserves my gratitude. I met her while visiting the wards in a local hospital. From her bed, she inspired me to make my experiences live on paper. She would accept nothing less than my best. Late into the night, she read my work and then made suggestions. She gave me technical advice on writing. Though she was a stranger to me, she became my teacher. Only later did I discover that she was a well-known journalist, author, and philanthropist.

Mrs. Virginia Lee, a member of my church, was also a constant source of inspiration and help. When I became discouraged, she became a support. When I seemed satisfied, she challenged my work. When I finished the manuscript, she painstakingly read and typed each page and assumed the drudgery aspect of preparing the manuscript, giving untold hours to this task.

Mr. John Seigenthaler, editor of *The Nashville Tennessean,* in the midst of his overwhelming daily schedule, read the finished manuscript and greatly aided my work with his measured suggestions and frank evaluations. Encouragement from a man of Mr. Seigenthaler's ability gave me a new sense of self-confidence.

To these and others who so graciously aided in my endeavor, I express my sincere appreciation.

# INTRODUCTION

Dear Chaplin,

I ain't much with words and I get a little tongue-tied when I try to say what I mean about something that's really important. I'd like to say this to you face-to-face, but maybe I can do it better in a letter. First off, you know the kind of guy I've been . . . I'm not gonna try to hide that. Everybody in the unit knows ole Gus, a big man, that's what I've tried to be. I guess I've fooled about everybody. The only thing really big about me has been my bluff. But, Chaplin, you and God saw through me and you made me see myself, and what I saw made me sick. You showed me one thing. I talked a lot about the hell of Viet Nam. It was in me. I didn't find it over here; I brought it with me. Chaplin, I don't know how to pray, but last night I told God to count me in. I've been such a slob I didn't want to ask a regular preacher like you to baptize me, so when nobody was watching I baptized myself in the creek. When I prove that I ain't kidding about all this, I want you to do it again the way it should be done.

A new member on God's team,
Gus

The spelling and wording in this letter are reproduced accurately from the original.

Before the letter reached the chaplain, the soldier was killed.

# Chapter One

## *"Raise Hell"*

As we worked our way single file through the thick under-growth of the jungle, I kept my eyes on the back of the sergeant just in front of me. If I lost sight of him for even a moment, I would call out in a hoarse whisper.

"Over here, Chaplain," he would answer. By this time he knew well the sound of my voice. I caught up again and stayed this time.

"I know how you feel, Chaplain, I don't intend to get lost either."

My helmet had a way of bouncing down over my eyes when I made a sudden turn. It was heavy, hot, and a constant source of irritation. To add to my discomfort, my pack was not properly strapped on. With every movement of my body the shoulder strap seemed to cut a little deeper into the blister on my back. And an examination of my left arm indicated that the scratches received from those "stickers" several days ago were infected. The cuts were red and puffed up.

I suddenly came upon the trooper in front of me. As he sat down on the ground, he called back over his shoulder, "Pass the word on, Chaplain, to hold up."

After passing the word along to the man behind, I took off my helmet, placed it on the ground, and sat on it with my back against a tree. What a relief to catch my breath and rest my back for a few minutes! Reaching around I unsnapped the harness on my pack and felt it fall away to the ground. The blister seemed to enjoy the change also.

After a brief moment, I looked around and noticed soldiers to my left and right spaced at intervals. Most of them were either sitting or lying. One was smoking, one opening a can of C-ration, and another was reading an old letter. A steady drizzle of rain was beating down, but the gloominess was pierced here and there by rays of sunlight which forced their way through the heavy foliage.

I became aware of my soaked shirt sticking to my body, so I unbuttoned it. The intermittent rains of the monsoon season in Viet Nam bathe everything with a sticky dampness.

I looked back at the ground over which we had just come. It was carpeted with fallen leaves, the rich green being replaced by the dull lifeless color of rottenness.

Determined to relax, I shut my eyes and leaned back against the tree. It's strange how noises are magnified out here. As I listened, the little inconsequential sounds which are always present but seldom noticed began to edge into my consciousness. The snapping of a limb, the rustling of leaves, the muffled clank of some metallic object seem as overwhelming to the senses here as the clanging of a firebell or the whining of a siren in a quiet village. My wandering thoughts were interrupted, and I was jolted back to reality by the familiar paratrooper greeting, "All the way, sir." I didn't need to open my eyes to recognize the source of this forceful and familiar voice. It had to be Private Ted Blake.

There he stood, six feet, four inches of muscled body. Two belts of ammunition encircled his broad chest, one over each shoulder and under the other arm, crossing in front. His green jungle fatigues had that usual sour odor which comes with several days wear, and his combat boots were caked with mud. Fastened on the web belt around his waist were several hand grenades, a machete, a canteen, a first-aid pouch, ammunition pouch, and an entrenching tool.

As he greeted me, he began to squirm out of his pack. Written across the front of his helmet was the word, "Airborne." An elastic band around the headgear held a package of C-ration cigarettes and a Hershey candy bar. Underneath this steel pot and sweaty uniform was an American soldier, one of the best in the world—the airborne infantry type, tough, aggressive, and daring. Young, not yet twenty, the vigor of his youth radiated from the top of his head to his size twelve combat boots.

"Hi, Ted, good to see you. Have a seat in my parlor."

"Chaplain, I can't sit down; I'm really 'teed off.' "

The flare of temper revealed in his words and the anger in his eyes prompted me to stand up. I'd only known Blake slightly, and I had never seen him angry or excited before. In fact, two weeks ago Sunday at base camp, I had met him for the first time.

He had attended one of my religious services and remained to talk to me. I well remember his first words, "I'm not the kind of guy who goes around talking to chaplains. In fact, I'm not sure what I'm doing here now, but I've got to talk to you." After I urged him to go on he continued, "Well, Chaplain, I heard this singing and I wondered what was making all that noise, so I walked over to where all those guys were sitting on the ground. Just then you started preaching. Chaplain, something you said really got to me, and I have to get it straightened out."

I asked him what was wrong, and before I could finish the question he added, "Chaplain, will you tell me how I can become a Christian? I just can't keep on like I have been going."

Although I was surprised at his frankness and directness, I had learned to appreciate this quality in young soldiers. We knelt down on the ground to pray, and I saw tears in his eyes.

Since that day, Ted Blake had become a changed person. He came by my tent several times asking help in understanding verses in the little New Testament I had given him. So now, as he stood before me, noticeably upset and shifting nervously from foot to foot, I knew that what concerned him must be serious.

"Chaplain, you remember Sutton who accepted Christ after one of your services? Well, just before we left for this operation I was in Bien Hoa on a pass. I happened to see him and he was boozing it up. It burned me up. He's just a little way behind us in the line here. I'm going back to get him and bring him to you and make him repent."

Before I could grasp what he was saying, he pivoted around to leave. "Wait a minute, Ted, you can't do that. You can't make a man repent."

As he hurried down the line, he looked back over his shoulder and shouted, "If you don't think so, Chaplain, just watch me."

I stood in amazement, staring at him as he disappeared from sight. Then, pondering this unorthodox situation, I heard a scrabbling noise down the line. Blake had Sutton by the arm, dragging him in my direction. It would be pointless to attempt to describe the expression on Sutton's face. And then the two soldiers stood in front of me. Before I could speak, and I am not sure what I would have said even if I had all the time in the world, Blake said in a solemn voice, "All right, Sutton, let's get down on our knees, you're gonna repent." As he spoke, he pushed down on his friend's shoulder and they dropped to their knees. Blake had his arm around the neck of his buddy. As I looked down at the two men, I could not help noticing Blake's arm, which was forcibly imprisoning his buddy as they prayed silently. Tattooed on his left biceps in big red letters were two words, "Raise Hell." The irony of it was perfect. This sturdy arm which had been a familiar sight in most of the dives near our base camp and which boldly advertised its intent in the big blazing tattooed letters, was now assisting a far less experienced sinner to repent.

After a few moments Blake asked me to pray. Sutton nodded assent. As I began to pray, I could not help but remember the words of another soldier named Paul who said, "If a man be in Christ, he is a new creature, old things are passed away, behold all things are become new."

"Dammit, anybody seen Blake?"

Blake and Sutton jumped to their feet. "I'm over here, Sergeant," Blake answered. He didn't need to ask who wanted him. He recognized the voice.

The sergeant walked over, "Well, now, isn't this nice? Just making yourself at home and visiting around? I didn't disturb you, did I?"

"I was just over here a minute, Sarge. I'm on my way back now."

"Now, that's real nice, Blake, and if I could have one minute of your time before your busy social schedule demands you elsewhere, I'd appreciate it."

The soldier blushed.

"Blake, I'd like to advise you that you'll be the point man when we move out. You wouldn't mind doing us this little favor, would you?"

"No, Sarge, but what's wrong with Milligan? I thought he was point man today."

A scowl formed on the sergeant's face. "He claims he turned his ankle." He emphasized the word *claimed*. "Now I ain't no doctor, but if you turn up with some ache or pain I might just create some pain in the seat of your pants. Get me?"

"I've got you, Sergeant, but don't waste your suspicions on me. When I get on the point, I'll stay there. It don't scare me none."

"All right, Blake. We're gonna move out in about an hour. Go

up and relieve Milligan pronto so you'll be all set when the Old
Man gives the word."

"Will do, Sarge." A small stream ran nearby. Blake walked
over to its edge and for a few moments just gazed at it. All of a
sudden his face lit up, and he moved eagerly toward me.

"Chaplain, would you do me a favor?"

"Sure, Ted."

"Remember, Chaplain, we talked about my being baptized but
were not able to line it up before we had to move out on another
operation?"

"Sure. It's tough to work out any kind of schedule over here,
but the day we get back. . ."

"I've got a better idea. Let's do it right now. We've got an
hour to kill, a stream to baptize in, a convert, and a preacher."

"You mean right now, right here, Ted?"

"Sure, why not? I want to be baptized."

I couldn't answer his "why not," so he stripped off his shirt,
and the next thing I knew he was standing in the stream not quite
waist deep with boots and pants still on, waiting for me. Why
he bothered to remove any clothing was a bit of a mystery in view
of the fact we were usually rained on most of the day.

A couple of men overheard Blake talking to me so they walked
over. One of them said, "Can you beat that? A baptism service
out here." Several other troopers had observed Blake standing in
the stream and had come closer to see what was going on.

I said, "Blake, if you like, we can just stand over here on the
ground by the side of the stream. I can get some water in my
helmet and sprinkle you for the baptism."

His answer came quickly and with conviction. "No, sir, I'm a
Baptist, and we believe in submersion."

I couldn't keep from chuckling. "You mean "immersion," don't
you?"

"Immersion and submersion, it's all the same, Chaplain, just
so I get all the way under the water. I don't want to be baptized
just halfway."

By this time we had a pretty good-sized congregation. Some
of the onlookers had never seen a baptism before, and others
were amused by the whole thing. I, myself, had never seen anything exactly like this. I waded to Blake's side, placed one hand
on his back and with the other I pressed downward on his hands

which were folded on his chest. As he was lowered into the water, I pronounced the ritual, "I baptize thee, my brother, in the name of the Father, and of the Son, and of the Holy Spirit."

Just as his face was at the point of being immersed, Blake stiffened up and made a slight unconscious attempt to keep his head and shoulders above water. I pressed a little harder, and his head went under but one arm still remained above the surface. The tattoo "Raise Hell" on the arm caught my attention. Shifting my hand to that shoulder, I pushed downward. That was one tattoo that was going to get the full "submersion."

As Blake's face reappeared, and he came to a standing position, my eyes caught sight of the sergeant standing a short distance off. He had his hands on his hips and was shaking his head from side to side in disbelief. I heard him say, "Well, I'll be damned." He just stood there with his mouth hanging open.

Blake slipped on his shirt, strapped on his gear, and then extended his hand in my direction. "Thanks, Chaplain," he said cheerfully. "I feel great."

We shook hands and I felt a kinship with this young soldier stronger than most men ever experience. "God bless you, Ted. Take care of yourself up there on the point. See you later."

"See you, Chaplain, thanks again." As he picked up his rifle and headed toward the front of the line, he waved good-by to me. "Let's keep our eyes on Sutton. He's not very strong yet, Chaplain." With these words he vanished into the jungle.

We still had about forty-five minutes left before moving out so I thought I would get off my feet for awhile, rest my legs, and perhaps get in some sermon preparation while I had the opportunity. I had my little Bible in a cellophane bag in my shirt pocket. Taking it out, I started thumbing through its pages.

"Chaplain, sir, if you don't beat all." A smiling Specialist-fourth class Albright squatted down by my side. Seeing that I was studying, he stood quickly to his feet. "Oh, pardon me, sir, I didn't realize that you were giving your attention to scholarly pursuits at the present moment. Please forgive the intrusion."

"Come on and sit down, Alex, I need a few pointers for my next sermon. Maybe you can suggest a quotation or poem that will help me illustrate my point. You read a lot, and from what I hear, you never forget anything that you read."

"I'm afraid, Chaplain, that most of my reading is on the other side of the question which you will be propounding in your sermon. I'm what you might call a religious eclectic. I more or less fluctuate between the philosophical foundations of agnosticism and atheism. While not committed to any one theory, I do try to be honest and open-minded in my examination of each of them. This very honesty prohibits me from standing in your corner theologically."

"I'm afraid you've lost me, Alex, with all of those high sounding terms. Anyway, what did you mean by that crack, 'If I don't beat all'?"

"You just interest me, sir. Here we are deep in the jungle on a search and destroy operation, in an area crawling with VC and what are you doing? Of all things, standing knee deep in a stream of dirty water baptizing a guy. If that doesn't take the cake. And if that's not enough, you don't even carry a weapon."

"I'm no hero, Alex, but what would I do with a weapon? You boys can handle that department. I'm just a preacher, that's all."

"Sir, you don't think your preaching will change things, do you? You can't really believe intellectually that speech making is the answer to this mess, or to any of the real issues for that matter. I'm inclined to think there is a whole lot more magic in my M-16 rifle than in that little black book you carry."

"Alex, why are you here at this spot today? Basically, isn't it because your commanding officer directed you to do so? Well, that's why I'm here. I feel that my commanding officer has commanded me to be here. I want to be as loyal to my God as any soldier can be to his general."

Albright looked like he wanted to argue, but he changed the subject. "Chaplain, just how did you end up over here? Why did you get involved in something like this? The name of this game is 'kill,' and I've got a feeling you'd even hesitate to squeeze the trigger if you did have a rifle and had it pointed right at a Viet Cong. Somehow, I can't visualize Christ being in khaki anyway."

"Hey, is Albright back here anywhere?" a voice called out. "The lieutenant wants him up front."

"I'll see you later, Chaplain, I'd like to have a more extended conversation with you along these lines at your convenience. All the way, sir."

"Anytime, Alex."

As Albright left, I lay on the ground, resting my head on my helmet. We'd be moving out shortly so I wanted to snatch a few more moments of rest. I had learned to relax during these breaks and found that by taking full advantage of the rest periods I was more alert and strong when on the move.

One statement of Albright's jumped into my mind. He had asked, "Why did you get involved in something like this?" To be perfectly honest I had often pondered this question in my own mind during these recent weeks. I knew I was exactly where God wanted me and although I felt normal anxiety, I experienced no actual fear for my life. But though I did possess a sense of divine certainty as to my particular mission here, I often reflected on the series of incidents that had been instrumental in placing me here.

Perhaps part of it is due simply to the nature with which I was born. As far back as I can remember, I had an overabundance of sensitivity. To me, anything that mattered at all mattered greatly.

When I graduated from the seminary, I accepted a small town church. My wife and I were very happy in our work. Three years later we were called to a large church, and it was after one year at this parish that something happened which swept me from a comfortable and enjoyable pastorate to this present jungle path.

Shortly after arriving at my new church, I met a young man who showed unusual promise. I suppose every minister has a deep desire to influence an outstanding young man to enter the ministry and I knew immediately that Dave Brown was to be the one. He was president of the senior class, a natural leader, and possessed a good mind. He was serious minded and reminded me a great deal of myself when I was his age.

You can imagine my delight when he confided in me that he was considering the ministry. He expressed the natural hesitation and feelings of unworthiness that most young men experience when being confronted with such a demanding and holy calling. We talked often and shared our feelings.

After a long period of reflection, Dave decided to go into the service before seeking admission into a seminary. He felt that he needed more maturity and experience before applying himself to theological studies. I hated to see him make this decision, but I respected his motives and admired his sincerity.

He joined the service and was sent to Viet Nam. But it wasn't long before that terrible telegram reached his home advising his parents that he had been killed in action.

A friend informed me of this tragic report, and I went quickly to the home of Mr. and Mrs. Brown. When Mrs. Brown saw me, she broke into tears. Very few words seemed to come. We were silent. I expressed my regrets and commented on what a fine boy Dave had been. They could be proud of him. I offered any help in any way and assured them of the prayers of our congregation. Mr. Brown walked out on the front porch with me—a broken man. As I departed, I remarked, "Harry, we understand how it is." The childlike sincerity in his answer haunted me. "Pastor, I wonder if anyone really does, except God?"

Upon returning home I looked over the sermon I would preach the next morning and then went to bed. There was to be no sleep that night. I cared so very much for this family, but did I even begin to understand? And then the theme of my sermon from Psalm 139 came into my mind. I was speaking on the subject, "Behold, God is There." How little we know of the troubles of those around us! But surely, whatever the trouble may be, God is right there in the middle of it, suffering along with us. The more I thought about my sermon, the less it seemed to matter in my situation. I was worried. What was I doing here?

During the course of my sermon I spoke of emotional hells and of the fact that God was always there. I wanted to understand, but how could I? I wasn't there. I loved my country, but in my position, how could I be there in Viet Nam? As quick as a flash the thought came, "If you really care, you'd *be* there." I don't know how I completed my sermon that morning.

As I read the morning paper day after day that week, all I could see was news about Viet Nam. Everyone with a relative in Viet Nam seemed to want to speak to me.

The next Sunday I had planned to preach on the topic, "Here Am I, Send Me." I couldn't do it. If God was going to be there with His children in this special kind of hell, He would need someone to represent Him. Someone to be sent.

I hoped this inner turbulence didn't show itself on my face. But I never could hide my feelings. My thoughts were interrupted by the soft and clear chiming of the hour. This was the signal that our worship service was about to begin. I bowed my head and asked God's blessing upon our worship. How I loved these people and how thrilled I had been when first called "pastor" by one of our elderly gentlemen. This thrill had never died.

The worship service always received my careful attention, but today, everything went wrong. I liked to read my prayers of invocation so as to make each one meaningful, but due to my preoccupation, I read last Sunday's prayer again. Probably no one noticed, but I did, and was embarrassed. In this momentary embarrassment I announced an incorrect number for the first hymn. So, for the first verse, our organist played one selection and the congregation attempted to sing another. This arrangement wasn't very satisfactory. Later in our responsive reading, things had settled down, when all of a sudden my eyes focused on the congregation's part of the reading instead of the minister's. To avoid embarrassing me, my gracious congregation confidently and with one voice then assumed the minister's part of the reading. Scattered smiles throughout the congregation assured me of their sympathy.

When we finally arrived at the beginning of the morning's sermon, I felt relieved, for preaching was natural to me. It was something to which I looked forward and gave a lot of preparation. I kept rather full notes, and on Saturday nights, after filling my mind and heart with the contents, I would fold these notes and place them within the back cover of my Bible.

Going into the pulpit is a joy experienced only by preachers who preach Sunday after Sunday and love every moment of it.

My inner anxiety of the past week was forgotten until I reached under the back cover of my Bible for my sermon notes. They weren't there! In a moment my memory relived the hours of the night before and in horror I could see those notes being placed in my large *study* Bible and could hear my conscience cautioning me to put the notes in my other Bible immediately. I couldn't forget anything so important and obvious as that. But I did!

My momentary silence caused individuals scattered across the sanctuary to look up. The usual cadence of the service was broken, and even the children wondered what was wrong. With extreme effort I mustered a smile. My congregation smiled back, and waited. I also waited. I smiled again, and they returned the smile, but this time every eye was on me and the present moment became electrified with expectancy. Here was the routine being replaced by the authentic, and it frightened me.

As I opened my mouth, I was surprised to hear my own voice saying, "This morning you will not hear 'preacher talk,' but instead, I want to talk to you as a fellow sinner." From there I poured out my heart expressing my desire to be in Viet Nam where the word of God needed to be preached. I wanted to give God the use of my life so that through me He might be there where He is needed. It was my intention to offer my resignation and go to Viet Nam as a chaplain. This was an irregular situation, I knew, and perhaps I had handled it badly, but some say Jesus Christ muffed His mission also.

My voice broke in my next sentence and my eyes were moist. I announced the final hymn and felt wonderful. While pronouncing the benediction, I added silently, "Thank you, God, for misplacing my sermon notes."

As was my custom, I stood outside the door and greeted the people as they departed. The emotions of my parishoners varied. One kind lady said she so hated to see me leave the ministry. A freckle-faced boy, Stevie, asked if I would tell his big brother stationed in Viet Nam that he had made the little league ball team. One of my most trusted friends asked me if I really felt that this move would be good for my career. As I started forming an answer, I felt a hand inside my arm. It was my wife, and her smile interpreted her tears. All of a sudden it was just great to be alive.

Harry Brown, Dave's father, had lingered in the sanctuary and walked out last. His hand gripped mine in a different way. "Pastor," he said, and his voice broke. Clearing his throat, he attempted to speak again. "Pastor," and the silence that followed said more than the most eloquent combination of words. He smiled through his tears and departed. As I left for home, it seemed that I stood a little taller. And as I asked the blessing over our noon meal, it seemed that God was listening, and I think He smiled.

The sergeant's shout broke the silence. "Saddle up, men, we're

ready to move out. I don't want to see anybody still sitting down when the CO says to move. All of you dig holes and bury your C-ration cans, cigarette butts, and all that other trash you've thrown around. I don't plan to get no third purple heart because some ignorant numbskull left a clear trail for the Congs to follow."

I stood up.

"Oh, I'm sorry, Chaplain," the sergeant apologized. "I didn't see you sitting there. O.K., dammit, do like I said, men. Don't just sit there. Get set to move out."

# Chapter Two

# Riding the "Point"

"Pass the word along to Blake to move out," the CO directed.

When the word worked its way up the column to Blake, he was ready. Arranging all his gear on his back, he picked his M-16 rifle in his right hand, and slowly and deliberately edged out in the prescribed direction. Private Blake would feel undressed without his M-16. It went with him everywhere. He cared for it like a mother would her baby. At any time it could be the deciding factor in his whole universe. He always kept it clicked on automatic so that just by squeezing the trigger once, he could fire a whole clip of bullets.

"Slow it down, Blake," a voice behind him called. "They say some of the guys in the rear can't keep up."

"O.K., O.K.," Blake knew sometimes how, when he became preoccupied with his thoughts, he would pick up speed. Probably he felt that by quickening the pace he could get out of this God-forsaken place a little sooner and get on back to base camp for a few extra days before the next operation. Base camp wasn't much to look forward to but at least it wasn't as bad as this.

"Blake, dammit, slow it down," another voice from the rear complained.

SP/4 Albright came up from the column. "Blake, the CO said to hold it up. Someone in the rear is having trouble."

The sergeant behind them quickly asserted, "Trouble, hell, they're just dragging, same as always."

No one had any doubt who was speaking. Sergeant Stagg's voice was always obnoxious. Anything he said seemed vulgar just because he said it. He had a twang in his speech that was irritating and a crude way of giving orders that indicated his brutish outlook on life. He never had conversation with an enlisted man; he ordered him. He never talked to an equal. Either he was correcting some underling or he was receiving an order issued by a superior. His title for most people was the same. "Hey, soldier, yea you." Often new soldiers, rattled by the loudness of his greeting, would reply, "Sir?" His favorite reply was, "Don't call me sir, soldier, I work for a living." The nickname given to Sergeant Stagg by the men and used as often as possible when he wasn't around, was "Sergeant Stagnant."

SP/4 Albright came up and sat down with Blake. "How's it going?" he asked.

"So, so. When are you supposed to get back up here, Albright?"

Albright frowned and grunted, "I ought to be up here now." His gaze penetrated the greenery up ahead. "I came out here to fight, and I'm tired of being stuck back in the rear."

These thoughts and the words used to express them seemed oddly out of character for SP/4 Alexander Albright. He was of medium size and a strikingly handsome Negro. His skin was dark but only enough to give him a light rich tan. He was immaculate in his grooming, and even in the filth and sweat of an operation such as this, he gave the appearance of just stepping on stage. But it was not a studied mannerism. On Albright it was natural. Nature seemed to have installed a glow about his person and painted a smile on his face.

Albright volunteered for every assignment and never missed a single operation. He asked repeatedly to be put on the point. Granted this was more than it should have been, perhaps because he did such a good job. And then, too, the competition was not keen for the kind of jobs he requested. The men were glad to have someone like him around because it moved them back one man from the front of the line. But the platoon leader, Lieutenant McNeil, had begun to suspect something and was a little more reluctant to grant Albright's requests. Perhaps he ought to have him see the doc. He might be needing a little rest. A week's leave might calm him down.

SP/4 Albright, brushing off the soil from his pants, said, "I'll be going on back now. We'll pass the word up when the other guys are set. Take it easy. See you." He disappeared quickly in the brush.

A short distance down the column, Captain Spence Brakowski, the CO, was talking to the radio and telephone operator who always followed closely at his elbow. The enlisted man had the communication equipment strapped on his back and kept the

CO informed of all incoming messages. The RTO, as he was called, must be an alert and responsible soldier. His radio equipment was the lifeline of the unit, and it had to be operated properly. Nothing could be said over the air that would compromise either their location or that of other friendly units because the enemy monitored almost every message sent out. The use of the various codes and call signs had to be mastered. There was no other way for units in distress to contact their command and pinpoint the location of the enemy for the benefit of possible air strikes or friendly artillery except through this RTO man. In addition to carrying this heavy cargo on his back, the RTO had to carry all his personal gear along with the standard weapon and ammunition. To complicate his job more, he had to become the shadow of the CO—not getting in his way but being right at his back when needed. Often the CO would walk along with the phone in his hand giving a steady flow of directions.

The captain didn't like having to stop, but he had notified the other columns to hold up for a second. He was an exceptionally good officer—fair but always demanding effectiveness from his men.

"I'll wait a second, and if things don't shape up in the rear, I'll check it out," he thought. The men in the rear of a column always have to move along at a faster rate just to keep up, so probably when Blake started stepping up the pace, one or two soldiers with extra heavy loads had found it increasingly difficult to hold their position in line. It is a standing rule to keep visual contact at all times with the man immediately to the front. Since beaten paths or trails are never followed for fear of mines or ambushes, the only available means of direction is the one soldier in front. At any instant he might make a sudden turn, and if at that moment the man behind him is not watching, every man in the column could get lost. Quite frequently, in the jungle, vision never extends for more than a couple of yards in any direction. Probably when one of the last few men saw the gap widening between them, they simply sent the word up the line to hold up for a few seconds so that everyone could catch up.

"RTO," Captain Brakowski called over his shoulder, "Get the platoon leader back there on the phone and see what's holding them up. It'll be dark in a few hours and we've got a couple of thousand meters to go yet."

"Yes, sir." And in a moment he called, "Lieutenant McNeil is on."

"Hello, Billy Joe, this is Ponderosa Papa, come in please. Over."

"Ponderosa Papa, this is Billy Joe. How are things at the ranch? Over," Lieutenant "Bull" McNeil, the platoon leader, replied.

Lieutenant McNeil's first name was Bill, but early in his college days he had been nicknamed "Bull" because of his fierce charging on the football field. He would lower his head and shoulders and make a weird snorting sound as he charged would-be tacklers. The lieutenant and Captain Brakowski had been classmates at university where both were outstanding students and athletes. They were the best of friends, which is why "Bull" had asked to be assigned to the captain's company when he arrived in the unit. Spence Brakowski had been nicknamed "Speed" on campus, and, during their senior year, he and "Bull" had given the team one of its best football seasons in years.

"Billy Joe, what's wrong back there? We don't have much more time to wait. Over."

"Sir, one of our new men had a little case of heat prostration, but I think he'll make it now after this rest. Over."

"Dammit, Billy Joe, see to it that those men take their salt tablets and drink plenty of water. It's got to be one or the other and they're just not watching it. No trooper of mine is gonna pass out and have to be carried by the rest of us, and you know there's no other way of getting him out of here. Can you move now? Over."

"Roger, Ponderosa Papa, everything's under control. Let's move. Over and out."

"Good going, Billy Joe, over and out."

Captain Brakowski gave the receiver to his RTO and said, "All right, saddle up and move out. Let's knock those other meters out and get a little hot chow before dark."

Sergeant Stagg picked up the CO's order and yelled, "O.K., O.K., you can thank those goof-offs in the rear for this time we've had to waste, but you're gonna earn your salary now. Move out."

The column was moving cautiously at its regular pace. Everything was as usual. Just another day of plodding forward on a mission to search for and destroy the enemy. But some wouldn't be too disturbed if they didn't find them. Many of the men were old-timers at it, tired and ready to have this nightmare end. But at the same time, they wanted to win the war. Some of the best buddies they had in this world had been part of the price to be paid so far. They owed it to them to even up the score just a little.

But the old-timers took no chances. They knew how serious and final this business was. And then, there were the men with just a few days or weeks left before their rotation date. The last operation was an emotional hurdle for every man. You didn't have to be superstitious to dread this one. Everyone knew several men who had gotten it on the last time out. As forbidding as was the thought of death, the fear of finally making it to almost within sight of home and family again but missing it was greater.

The men who are relatively new can probably be divided into two distinct classes. Those who are terrified at the thought of it all and those who don't really sense much fear. The ones who are terrified bring with them all the war stories picked up back in the States. Every unusual sound, every crack of a weapon, every step through the jungle plunges them into torment. Somewhere along the line they accept the fact that there are only two ways back home—in a box or making it through the required twelve months. Their one ambition is to make it. The torment doesn't change; they just learn to keep going.

Those who don't seem to sense any fear simply don't understand the silent abyss over which they tread in their casual and cocky innocence. It takes only a few operations to gain a solemn respect for an unidentified chance noise in the distance, a silence that is too silent, or just that "feeling" that has often been too true. In this university men gain their degrees quickly. And with tragic swiftness the report cards of dropouts are received by their heartbroken families in the form of official notification of regrets and condolences from the United States Government.

One by one the men push on forward as the long column creeps through the jungle toward its destination. From a distance they are a forbidding and disturbing sight, as are all soldiers, armed and ready for combat. Most of the soldiers of any country in the world would be sickened and distressed if they could see themselves from a distance. What a ghastly and absurd business is war!

They are molded into soldiers, informed as to what they must defend and of the justice of their cause. Equipped with the implements of death, they are skilled in turning all of this into a nightmare that attempts to destroy everyone outfitted in a different colored uniform. On the outside they are soldiers and press on courageously to win, but increasingly through the battles and the suffering and the killing—and the winning and the losing—a thought steals across their minds that the more noble the victory, the more glaring is the actual defeat. But perhaps, the most ironic note of all is that, as clearly as the futility and insanity of all the wars of the past can be seen, we become caught up in the context of our own war and it not only seems feasible, but inevitable and right.

Suddenly, with all the fury of a lightning bolt we were deafened by a loud explosion. A scent of gunpowder mushroomed instantly through the atmosphere. Red hot projectiles of twisted jagged metal could be heard thudding into tree trunks, tearing through foliage, and whipping by overhead. Every man hit the ground, and then there was that awful silence. One soldier made a slight movement.

"Stay down," said a commanding voice from the rear.

And then that terrible stillness hung over us as though waiting for something dreadful to happen.

# Chapter Three

# They're Out There Somewhere

The heavy stillness was punctured by two sounds. The first was a soft muffled zing nearby. A quick movement was seen in the grass, and then the familiar voice of little Pete was heard.

"I'm hit," he muttered.

These two words conveyed the feeling of one who had just made a painful discovery. A discovery that seemed beyond the realm of possibility. It was almost more of a question than a statement, as though a man would ask a question that he wanted someone to contest, hoping maybe there was a chance that he could be mistaken.

And then as amazement gave way to realization, Pete cried out, "I'm hit, I'm hit, somebody help me, I'm hit."

Pete had scarcely realized he had been hit in the leg during the excitement of that first impact, but when his eyes detected the circle of blood forming on his mud-soaked pants, his imagination sent flashes of pain through his body.

Sergeant Stagg, who was lying near by, crawled through the brush to Pete's side.

"How are you, boy? Did you get in the way of something?"

"It's my leg, Sarge, it hurts. I don't know how bad it is."

The sergeant tore the cloth away from the wound, and then smiled, "Everything will be all right. Don't worry, it's just a little scratch." And his usual note of impatience, he added, "Don't lie here and bellyache all day; you'll live. Report to the medic. And don't think you're gonna git out of anything with a little hit like that."

But these words were forgotten as a shout came from somewhere up toward the front of the column. It was, "Medic," repeated three times in rapid succession—a word everyone dreaded to hear. There was a haunting ring to it—a constant reminder of the razor-sharp, cutting edge of combat. It shattered the hope that perhaps this time everyone had made it through all right. That penetrating call meant that someone had fallen—someone

had been "zapped." No one knew how bad it was, whether the
man involved was living or dead, but the word was like an alarm
siren.

On the other hand, those same words brought a kind of eerie
comfort to each soldier. Deep in the breast of every man was
the fear that he would be wounded and defenseless and have to
watch helplessly as life bled from his body. There was the horror
that he would be abandoned and become easy prey to the Viet
Cong. The constant nightmare was that his body would be left
behind as his buddies withdrew.

So, the word "Medic" becomes more than a call of desperation. It is a sacred covenant understood and honored by every
man. The call will never go unheeded. The prayer will never go
unanswered. It is like presenting a claim check at the window
and withdrawing a commodity that is guaranteed to every man,
woman, and child in America, the right to live. What an unusual experience—to learn about the great traditions of our country lying wounded in a rice paddy or jungle thicket eight or ten
thousand miles from home. This muddy bed in hell is a strange
classroom in which to be reminded of the sacred principles that
have motivated America since her earliest history.

So when a solitary soldier calls for help, he does it with an
expectation put there by a faith in his country—a faith made
substantial by such basic truths as, "We are endowed by our
Creator with certain inalienable rights, that among these rights
are life, liberty, and pursuit of happiness." When the call goes
out for the medic, the soldier knows that a man with a medic's
bag strapped on his back will come to his aid, even in the face
of direct fire. If this medic becomes a casualty, another will take
his place. It helps a man to go out again and again, just knowing
that in one way or another he will always make it back, thanks
to the medics.

The call for the medic jarred everything to life and heads
popped out from behind trees and out of gullies. A medic moved
quickly from the rear.

A voice called, "Stay down, get out of the way, let the medic
by." At first he crouched cautiously under cover, as if he expected his movement to draw fire. When no fire came, he moved
more boldly along the column.

As he passed, men crouching on the side would point forward

and say, "That way, Medic." At the very head of the column he was signaled by a trooper who was kneeling at the base of a tree.

"Over here, Medic," he called. "It's Blake, the point man. I heard the explosion and was knocked down," he continued, "and then I started calling for Blake but he never answered."

"Are you O.K.?" the medic asked.

"Yeah, but let's check on Blake."

The soldier then called back down the column and asked for some men to be sent to secure the area immediately up ahead, since snipers might still be there. Several troopers moved up quickly and fanned out in the general direction of the explosion.

"Watch it now," one of the men warned, "the 'gooks' may be waiting for us."

"All right men, take your time, watch where you step," Lieutenant McNeil commanded, knowing full well the tragic consequences of a moment of carelessness.

From time to time a movement in the bushes could be heard—a broken twig or a word of assurance from one of the troopers to the man next to him. "Over here," one of the men yelled. "Oh my God, here he is."

"Medic, over here."

Instantly the medic ran toward the sound of the two voices.

"Over here, over here, we've found Blake."

The medic saw two men kneeling over a third one. They moved aside as he approached. The sight on the ground was sickening. Blake was lying face down. Across his back numerous shrapnel wounds dotted his shirt, each one blood-soaked. His left arm was almost severed. The medic, SP/4 Peavy, carefully turned the body over on its back. The two men watching had to turn away. One of them stepped back, glanced again at the body, and threw up.

The medic muttered, "Blake got it right in the face and stomach."

About the only thing recognizable was the tattoo on his upper left arm—big red letters spelling the two words, "Raise Hell."

"Can you do anything for him, doc?" the third soldier asked.

"You haven't seen him yet, have you, buddy? Then don't look," the medic said grimly. "Get his poncho and put it over him while I gather his gear together." He hadn't been a medic for very long and this sort of thing still got to him. Filling out a brief

KIA, Killed In Action Report, he gave the pertinent information as to the date and circumstances of death:

By this time a number of troopers had gathered around, and as the plastic poncho was being placed over the body, first one and then another would look at Blake.

"I was just talking to him this morning," one youngster was heard to say.

Another passed a message down the line, "It's Blake; he's dead."

Sergeant Stagg bellowed out, "Don't bunch up around here, dammit, scatter out. Don't forget everything you've ever learned just because you've seen your first man killed."

"But, Sarge, have you seen him? Have you seen what he looks like?" one of the men cried, surprised that the sergeant could be so unmoved by this ghastly sight.

"Knock it off, trooper," Sergeant Stagg replied, "No, I haven't seen him and I don't intend to. He's dead and there's nothing we can do about it. Standing here and looking down at him like a bunch of sick kids won't bring him back to life neither, but it will get the rest of us killed. Now unless you've got some business here move on out so the rest of us can get our job done."

"That dirty - - -," one of the men muttered under his breath. "When he gets his, I won't even slow down. I'll just step over him like I would over a rotten log and keep going."

By this time, I had reached Blake's body. Kneeling beside him, I closed my eyes and held his lifeless hand in mine. My friend and spiritual son lay here dead. At that moment war became real to me.

The CO motioned for the sergeant. "Here, have some of your men look around and see if they can find out how this was done."

The sergeant answered, "Sir, we've already found a piece of trip wire. He must have tripped it over there by those vines and they had the Claymore mine aimed to go off right through here."

"Good, Sergeant," Captain Brakowski responded, "see what else you can find."

Some of the men had inserted sturdy tree branches lengthwise through the poncho in which the body had been wrapped and were preparing to move out. Lieutenant McNeil reminded the sergeant to be sure Blake's weapon and ammunition had been policed up. Frequently, as we had inspected Viet Cong bodies killed in some encounter, we would find U. S. Army clothing, weapons, and ammunition that they had been using—articles that our men had overlooked when we moved our casualties out days or weeks before.

"Check the area carefully, and don't leave one thing those 'gooks' can use against us. Then saddle up and move out," the CO directed. The long column began to move forward again. A new point man was put in position by the sergeant.

"Now, boy, watch your step. There're other mines around here just like that one. I haven't taught you a damn thing yet so don't go getting killed until I have time to make a real soldier out of you," Sergeant Stagg said gruffly.

The line proceeded further into the jungle. The weight of the motionless corpse, carried on the improvised stretcher, made the branches sag in the middle. Its swaying motion caused the two men to stumble and scramble uneasily to keep their footing. Sharp protruding limbs and prickly briars tore at the poncho, whipping and puncturing, causing the men to struggle desperately to avoid tipping the stretcher and dropping the body. Under the difficulty and tension of their task neither of the two men noticed the lifeless arm dangling over the side and dragging along the ground. "Hey, hold it a second," one of the soldiers called. He came alongside and gently placed the arm within the poncho.

"I'll take over awhile now. Bill, you carry the other end and let's give these guys some relief," he added.

The body was shifted from the hands of the first two men to the new troopers. Slowly the entire column faded into the jungle.

At 1700 hours, about an hour and a half before dark, the unit moved into the preselected bivouac area for the night. Usually these areas were chosen by the commanding officer when he made reconnaissance from the air several days prior to the operation. An area was chosen whose features indicate a maximum degree of security and which would also provide a clearing large enough for helicopters to set down, bring in supplies and mail, and take out the wounded, the dead, and other personnel who had to return to base camp.

Bravo Company was given the responsibility of securing the area. Each of the three rifle companies stayed in close radio contact with the battalion commander who was traveling with headquarters company. The other companies were given the order to hold up as Bravo Company slowly moved to the edge of the field. Small patrols were first sent out to "recon" the area. Any contact with the enemy was to be reported immediately.

No contact was made. More men were moved into the area and a perimeter guard was set up. This progress was radioed back to the Command Group, and the other companies were told to proceed to the area. Very soon the various companies began forming up in their designated locations. Each company must be in sight of the next one, thus encircling the clearing and apportioning an area of responsibility in setting up and providing security for the entire battalion.

As the men emerged from the jungle, they looked like endless lines of ants coming from all directions. The lines grew larger and larger and soon, as supplies and equipment were stacked here and there and as small groups of men were assigned to various activities, it looked more and more like a huge ant hill with all its attendant motion and liveliness.

Orders were snapped. The men were told to dig in, so entrenching tools shoveled dirt and holes appeared everywhere.

"Get it deeper, soldier . . . Not so close together, move over here . . . Don't make such a good target for them, all clustered up together like fat rats."

Several mortars were set up in the clearing so as to have a good line of fire. These mortars were accurate and could lay a screen of exploding shells in the face of any charging enemy. Frequently, they were given an assignment to fire all through the night at irregular intervals—out in all directions just to discourage any enemy probing of the area. If any movement was detected outside the perimeter, they could also drop a couple of eggs right on that spot with amazing accuracy.

On the perimeter area a line of defense was set up with riflemen, mortars, and heavy machine guns. Men were dug in deep, and in groups of two they occupied their "home" for the evening. Ammunition was stacked within the dugout. During the night one man slept while the other pulled guard. Most men slept in their clothes and boots.

The familiar sound of a helicopter made everyone look up. There it was, circling high above the clearing. The chopper had been radioed our exact location and was now coming in with supplies. It was almost like a long lost friend of the family unexpectedly dropping in. This was about the only contact with civilization we had experienced that day. Compared to our seclusion in the canopy-covered jungle all day, the base camp, from which it had come, only ten minutes away by air, seemed like civilization. While immersed in the nothingness of this nameless stretch of trees and vines, the friendly chopper above had become our only tie with something. So, as everyone looked up toward the descending aircraft, a new sense of belonging and hope welled up within. The very presence of the chopper verified our hopes that though we may feel lost, our higher command knows exactly where we are.

Three rifle rounds whizzed past the chopper as it made its final approach before touching down—a reminder that snipers could be anywhere in the green of the jungle around us.

After the rifle fire there was silence. What did it mean? It could be just a distant sniper hoping for a lucky shot. It could be the probing shots of a small VC patrol attempting to draw our fire and thus estimate the positions of our men and weapons. Or it could be the first shots of a fight that would bring hordes of Viet Cong pouring in upon us. The seconds of waiting were painful, but no more shots came.

As the chopper dropped to treetop level, the propellor sent gusts of wind into the ground below. Rotten limbs broke from trees and crashed down. Stinging sand sprayed across the field and clouds of dust mushroomed out. Ponchos were torn from their stakes. The men swore as they saw their bedding and personal gear covered with dust or scattered across the clearing.

When the chopper finally touched down, the motor was idled. Had the dust been white, the scene would have been that of a beautiful, snow-covered jungle. Instead, it was just plain dust, stifling and irritating—with burning eyes, hayfever coughs, and dust-caked faces in evidence everywhere.

The moment it touched down men raced toward it to unload the cargo. They lifted out cans of water, boxes of ammunition, and cases of C-rations. An assembly line was set up, and almost immediately the aircraft was empty. Three enlisted men jumped cautiously from the plane and stood awkwardly as though waiting for someone to tell them what to do.

"Hey, hold it up a second," the sergeant yelled to one of the crew members, "we've got a KIA to send in. Well, what are you three standing here for, want your picture taken or something?"

"No, Sergeant," one of the three soldiers volunteered. "We just arrived in the unit today from the States and they sent us on out here."

"All right, throw your gear down over there and help get these supplies moved under cover," the NCO said hurriedly. He added, pointing to two of the new men, "You, go over there and get the KIA and put it on the chopper."

The soldiers hurried off in the general direction the sergeant had pointed. They had no idea what a KIA was, but they weren't about to ask.

"Where's the KIA?" one of them asked a nearby G.I., trying by the tone of his voice to assume a casual air.

"Right behind you, buddy. You're not blind, are you?"

Looking around, he saw the poncho covering the body of the dead soldier. However, he did not know what was under the sheet of plastic, even though two combat boots protruded from the end.

The man, assuming that the KIA referred to must be a package of discarded gear, said to his partner, "Come on, let's get this stuff on the plane."

He reached down and snatched open the folded poncho. The sudden sight of the body literally froze the soldier in his tracks. The surprise and horror of it hit him so emotionally and with such sudden force that he crumpled to the ground in shock. He lay there muttering and sobbing, shaking uncontrollably. The man who was assisting gasped, stepped back as if to gather his composure, and then with a face paled by a new experience almost beyond his depth, leaned forward and covered the body.

The company first sergeant rushed over. "Two of you men take the body over to the chopper," he said, as he knelt by the side of the soldier who was in shock. "Take it easy, son, you'll be all right. Just lie right there and stay comfortable." He loosened the boy's shirt and put a rolled-up poncho under his head. "Son, you go and get the medic," he directed the young trooper who was staring down at his fellow recruit.

In just a few minutes the medic arrived. "What's the trouble, Sergeant Goodman?" he asked.

"This is one of our new men, just arrived on the chopper. He got too good of a look at the KIA, and I think he almost went into shock."

The medic bent down on one knee and examined the soldier carefully.

"He's pretty well shaken up, Sergeant, but I think he'll be O.K."

"I'm gonna send him back in," the sergeant said, "we can do without him for a few more days. Just note that he is to be on light duty around the base camp, and ask that he be checked out by the doc before he comes back to the field." After a moment's reflection he continued, "Still better, Peavy, let's put him on a stretcher and just send him in to the hospital for observation right now."

"Good idea, Sarge," Medic Private Shorty Peavy answered.

"And, by the way, Shorty, let's get Pete in to have his leg checked."

So, in not more than three minutes after the helicopter had touched down it had been emptied and was now lifting off again with the KIA, the soldier in shock, and Pete on board.

But before the dust had settled from the chopper lifting off, the sand was again stinging across the LZ (the landing zone) from two other helicopters making their descent. As they set down and idled their motors, men ran to unload the cargo quickly in order to get the aircraft back upstairs before they became too tempting for the Viet Cong.

One of the 'copter men yelled, "Send us some more help to get this hot chow off." Both choppers were loaded with steel containers of steaming food.

This was one thing that helped to keep the morale of the troops so high in Viet Nam. The food was good, even though it wasn't like Mom used to cook. Then, too, it wasn't what we might have preferred on any particular day, and no matter what it was, we griped like any red-blooded trooper is expected to do, but it was suprisingly good. Out in the field on operations the availability of food was especially important. Ordinarily, when the men departed on an operation, each took enough C-rations for two meals. C-rations were canned foods packed in cardboard boxes with sufficient food for one balanced meal. Each box contained canned meat, crackers, and a dessert, as well as gum, cigarettes, toilet tissue, matches, and instant coffee. A large variety of cans were available, but after a little experience the soldiers learned to detect the boxes containing the more choice menus. Some of the newer soldiers were unable to figure out why they never seemed to end up with the fruit cocktail, or the hot chocolate, or the pound cake. But they learned, hence there was always a rush when the C-ration cases were passed out, and then, of course, a great deal of trading transpired. Day by day we were supplied from the air with C-rations and never really had to be concerned about a shortage of food. Even if the helicopters were unable to find an adequate landing zone in the dense jungle, they could drop boxes of food and plastic cans of water from the air as they hovered above the trees. The cans might be bent and the crackers and cookies broken, but we would not go hungry.

But the real morale booster was just the fact that almost every evening during an operation, hot food was flown out to us wherever we were. This food was just off the stoves back at base camp and was sent immediately to the men. Hot coffee and iced tea also accompanied the chow. All the containers were unloaded in the landing zone and then dispensed quickly to the various companies. Each company would then set up its own mess line. After a few months in the field the C-rations seemed to lose their taste, and no one really anticipated the next meal. C-rations were just something to put in your mouth when someone said, "Let's eat while we have time." Occasionally, when someone would light a small heat tablet and place a can of beef stew over it, the aroma would create an appetite, but realizing the limited range of selections, a man would just light up a cigarette or take out a cookie. Having the senses so keyed up and being on the move so continuously discouraged giving much attention to eating. It was not unusual for many men to drink only a can of coffee for breakfast and eat one or two cookies for lunch. During a stay in Viet Nam many soldiers lose as much as forty to fifty pounds.

But in spite of everything, the one highlight of each day was that hot chow for supper. It was something to look forward to— a point at which you could strike one more day off your stay in Viet Nam. It is strange how significant something can become that just a few weeks or months before was too trivial to consider. Just a few months earlier it would have been impossible to imagine that the most prized event of the day would be sitting cross-legged on the dusty ground with a paper plate full of food that you would have passed up at any other time and drinking a canteen cup of weak, lukewarm tea.

As the containers were unloaded from the aircraft, one of the men yelled enthusiastically, "Hot dog, hot chow."

A young man standing some distance away partially overheard the comment and picked up the word, "Say, we've got hot dogs for chow today."

A trooper, overhearing the latest rumor, grunted, "Hell, hot dogs for chow. What do they think we're doing out here, walking around at a carnival? I'll bet they have cotton candy, too."

Men from various companies had been sent in to get the chow and were now carrying the large containers back to their units. Soon, all the rations disappeared except those that had been left for headquarters and headquarters company on the LZ.

The men from Alpha Company hurried toward their company area with their containers. The soldiers they passed couldn't help inquiring what the chow was tonight. The aroma of a hot cooked meal trailed along behind them and troopers seemed to pop out from behind every tree and follow these "pied-pipers."

"Sergeant Stagg, what about getting me five men to serve chow," Sergeant Goodman asked as he helped get the heavy cans in place.

"Sure will," Stagg replied as he pointed to the nearest five men and bellowed, "O.K., you, you, you, you, and you come over here. You just volunteered to be our mess crew tonight." Before they could respond, he yelled out, "All right, all right, don't just stand there with your bare faces hanging out. Move!"

The tops were taken off the containers and a man stood behind each one to dish out the food with a large spoon. At the end of the line were slices of white bread, a box of apples, chilled orange juice or hot coffee, and some melting cakes of chocolate ice cream.

"Come and get it while it's hot. Chow's ready," First Sergeant Goodman announced.

"All right, get it and get out," the gruff voice of Sergeant Stagg added. "The Geneva Treaty don't say they can't shoot just because we're eating."

As each man went through the line, he was given a portion of food and promptly moved along. Several were sitting together out in the corner of a little field.

"Soldiers, it'd be better if you didn't bunch up like that. Kinda spread it out and don't expose yourself any more than necessary," the first sergeant cautioned.

Sergeant Goodman lived up to his name. He was a good man. Though many years of being a professional soldier and fifteen years of being a first sergeant had put a certain quality of firmness in his voice that could literally petrify a soldier when the sergeant wished to use it, and though by nature he was a big man—husky in appearance, with hairy arms and chest—still you just didn't think of him as the first sergeant type. On a few occasions some new soldiers mistook his gentle manner for softness and attempted to take advantage of him, but they soon discovered their error in judgment.

The fact was, Sergeant Goodman was just so good, his spirit so captivating, and his personal interest in each of his men so sincere, that very seldom did the occasion ever arise for him to raise his voice.

As would be expected, many of the other sergeants thought he was too soft on his men—that he didn't harass them enough. "Take it easy on them and they'll make you look like a fool," they told him.

But he always gave his men the benefit of the doubt. His homespun philosophy was, "Treat a man like he really amounts to something and you'll find that he *will* amount to something."

"They're gonna make a sucker out of you yet, Goodman," one of his fellow first sergeants told him.

"Maybe so, maybe so, but I'm willing to take a chance on them," he would reply.

There were times when it appeared that the others were right and he was wrong. Some young trooper, still wet behind the ears, would take him for a soft touch. Some company dud would give him a sob story. Some undisciplined youngster, after having carelessly thrown away his money, would prevail upon the first sergeant to make a little loan.

Through the years many payments never came in and many touching stories proved to be only the marriage between a present predicament and an active imagination. But when he suffered, he suffered in silence. The strange thing, though, was the amazing way in which a company straightened out when Sergeant Goodman took over, the way in which long standing duds became effective soldiers, and the way in which the unit's morale picked up immediately and stayed that way. Some said it was luck. If so, his luck was consistent.

Without warning a heavy rain began to fall. The men scattered in all directions, some lucky ones finding shelter under ponchos. But the men who were still going through the chow line continued as though nothing had happened. In moments they were soaked, and with beads of rain running down their foreheads, they sat on the ground and munched their weiners and drank their cold tea.

Some of the men had been wet so often that they now gave no special attention to the rain. When they first arrived in Viet Nam, they would try to dodge every shower. But after months of downpours it just didn't seem to matter any more. Jungle fatigues were government issue, all were exactly alike—well-worn after a few operations—so any particular stress on individual distinctiveness was forgotten. Everyone was basically the same—fatigues, combat boots, dog tag, and crew cut. Though airborne troopers were expected to shave daily even on combat operations and to keep as neat as possible, such amenities became academic. So what difference did a little rain make? Nobody was going anywhere anyway.

"Mail call," a soldier shouted.

"Wouldn't you know it?" SP/4 Albright retorted. "No mail in two days and now when the bottom falls out of the sky the mail comes in."

The men didn't mind getting wet themselves, but they didn't want their letters to get wet. Mail call was an exciting and suspenseful time. The weakest were strengthened by getting a little encouragement from home, and the strongest were weakened when day after day no letter came. There were perhaps more wars fought in the minds and hearts of the men at mail call than in actual combat.

The majority of the men crowded around the soldier with the mail. A few others stayed under their ponchos, straining their ears to catch their names if they were called out. As each name was called, an eager trooper leaped forward, clutched the letter, and waited hopefully for more.

"Private Ted Blake," the soldier yelled out.

A hush fell over the group.

The soldier called again, "All right, Blake, if you want your letter, sound off."

"I'll take it for him," I said from the rear of the group.

Casually, the mail carrier flipped the letter over his shoulder saying, "Pass it on back."

It hit the shoulder of one of the troopers and fell to the ground as I reached for it. Rain splashed across the face of the letter blurring the ink. The return address was a Mrs. J. T. Blake, probably Ted's mother. I put the letter inside my shirt.

As I thought about the official notification that the Blakes would receive from the government telling them of the death of their son, it seemed terribly inadequate. There are some things that a stranger has no right to say, however sincere he may be. I thanked God that I had known Ted well enough to write his parents as a friend and tell them the kind of things that a mother and a father needed to hear.

When the last letter was passed out, the crowd quickly disappeared. The men with letters and packages found a dry place and started opening up their mail. The rain continued to pour down.

I crawled under a low-slung poncho where my enlisted assistant, Private Jimmy Hill, was already sprawled out on his air mattress reading his mail.

"Well, Jimmy, I had a letter come through today. I guess that puts me one up on you."

"I hate to lower your morale, Chaplain, but I got four letters today."

"You'll have to turn three of those letters back in, Private. You know that an enlisted man is authorized to get only as many letters as his supervisory officer."

"If I let you read mine, Chaplain, may I have them back?"

"Jimmy, you just keep them. All that mush those girls write you would probably embarrass me anyway."

I opened my letter with anticipation. It was mimeographed, and my enthusiasm was dulled since such letters are seldom personal. It was from the ministerial association in the city where I had last served as pastor. They had sent this invitation to their monthly meeting to my last church address and the church had forwarded it to me in Viet Nam. Since an airmail stamp had not been placed on the letter, the ministerial meeting had been over thirty-three days when I finally received the correspondence. The speaker for the program was to be a Dr. Wesley, who had recently made a two weeks' tour of Viet Nam. He was to speak on the topic, "The Ethics of Our Involvement In Viet Nam."

"Think I'll slip around the area and see how our troopers are making out."

"Say, Chaplain, drop over a second and I'll show you something," someone called.

I stopped and looked around to locate the direction of the voice. Under a poncho, half hidden by a clump of bushes, was Sergeant Stagg.

"Come on in, Chaplain, and I'll give you a cup of coffee. Cream and sugar?"

"Save your sugar, Sergeant. I have some here in my pocket."

Stagg had heated water in two small cans over a heat tablet. Small packets of instant coffee poured into each can produced a fair imitation of the real thing. It wasn't good by any stretch of the imagination, but it was hot and comforting. Somehow, a cup of coffee made everything seem a little more civilized.

"Chaplain, take a look at the letter I received today. It's kinda down your line. I thought you'd be interested."

The letter began, "Dear Junior, we are attempting to purchase new pews for our church. In order to make this purchase before our annual homecoming day we will need to acquire the needed funds within the next two months. One hundred dollars per member has been suggested as our goal. We would appreciate hearing from you and thank you in advance for your contribution to this worthy undertaking."

The letter was signed by the clerk of the church.

"Sergeant, I've never noticed you in our chapel services so I assumed you weren't interested, but I'm sure glad to learn of this."

"Well, Chaplain, as you know, I'm sure, I'm not the religious type. Before I came into the service I attended this country church out near our house. I wasn't very regular, but they must still have my name on roll. You know, it's sure a hell of a note to ask a man way out here for money, isn't it?"

I suggested that they would not have felt free to make such a request had they not felt close to him.

"How is everything else going, Sergeant Stagg? How's the family back home?"

"Not so good, Chaplain, I've got another letter I'd like for you to read. Looks like my wife is about to leave me."

I took the letter pushed toward me by the sergeant. "Shall I read just part of it?"

"No, sir, just read it all. It's short and to the point."

The letter read, "Dear Honey, how are things over there? Fine, I hope. They are about the same back here. I hate to tell you this but I might as well be honest for a change. I'm going to leave you. I know you can't help being over there and I can't help being like I am neither. You know what I mean. I need a man. I have waited as long as I can. You know I love you, but I just can't wait any longer. You knew how I was when you married me. The kids said to say hello. Love, Betty Jo. P.S. Harry said to remind you about the $5.00 you owe him."

"How do you feel about the letter?"

"Oh, she means it. She means every word of it."

"How was your relationship when you were back home?" I asked.

"I just didn't take nothing off her, Chaplain," he said, as if trying to give the impression that the whole situation was a fairly incidental matter. "My feeling is that you got to let a woman know who's boss. If she wants another man, let her go ahead. She knows I can get me a slant-eye over here with no problem at all."

"How often do you write your wife?"

"I don't guess I'm much of a writer."

Placing my hand on Stagg's shoulder, I suggested, "Sergeant, why not try an experiment. Write your wife, tell her that you love her, and let's see what happens."

Our conversation was interrupted as Captain Brakowski's voice broke in, "Come on, Chaplain, the colonel wants to have a staff meeting in ten minutes."

"Be right with you, Captain." I replied.

Speaking to the sergeant, I said softly, "What do you say, let's give it a try." Stagg turned away, giving me no indication of what he might do.

As the company commander and I walked through the woods to the command area, we passed by several enemy mines which had been detected and roped off.

"Boy, I'd sure hate to stumble on to one of those things," the captain said.

When we arrived at the designated area, most of the company commanders and staff members had already assembled. The colonel nodded and the first staff member, the S-3 who is in charge of plans and operations, gave a rundown of the day's activities.

He then outlined the plan for the next day. "Tomorrow at 0630 hours Alpha Company will move out. At the same time, on their right flank, Charlie Company will move out. Following Alpha Company will be headquarters and headquarters company and Bravo Company will be on their right flank.

"If we are hit, it will probably be from the right side since we have a report that there may be a company size VC unit somewhere off to the right. The area is mined so watch your step. Expect light sniper fire. We will pass through three villages tomorrow and should also find a training area. Do no damage to the villages. Don't fire unless you're fired at—then be sure of your target. Stay off all trails and paths; they will be mined. When we hit the training site, destroy everything they can use. Now, any questions?"

Several routine questions were asked and answered, grid coordinates were rechecked on the maps, and various items were discussed.

The S-2 officer in charge of intelligence gave a rundown on the weather and the latest data received from agents' reports concerning our immediate area.

"Any documents or materials that are found in the villages or the training area must be sent to me immediately. Be sure that your men realize that no item, I repeat, absolutely no item, can become their souvenir or personal property until it has been cleared through my section. Also, alert your men to the fact that VC are leaving weapons around and wiring them. They will explode if moved. Be extremely careful. And the last thing, police up the area tomorrow morning before leaving. Leave nothing that is usable and bury what you don't take. And, by the way, we have been having too much noise out here at night, so let's see if we can't keep it down."

The S-4 representative in charge of supply reported, "Tomorrow morning by 0530 I want all the water cans assembled here on the LZ. These cans cannot be left behind, and they must be available to be hauled out when the chopper comes in. Now, if your men continue to drag their feet, they'll find themselves carrying cans on their backs tomorrow. What's left when the chopper moves out will have to be carried. The VC can make some mighty potent weapons out of all that metal."

Following the regular reports by each of the four company commanders, the colonel stood up, "Gentlemen, I'd like to make just two or three comments. First of all, we had a KIA today. Each man counts to someone, and some mother will have her heart broken in a few hours when she is notified of the death of her son. Now I want to ask you a question. Was there any real reason why this man should have died? Think about it awhile. We found where the mine was hidden and we found the position of the trip wire. The man himself should have found it. By this time we should be professionals at this sort of thing. The mine was positioned just like they always do it and yet one of our seasoned troopers walked right over it. Gentlemen, their job was sloppy today compared to what we can expect in the future, and if we can't learn to handle these simple ones, what are we going to do when things get tougher? Now, I'm not directing these remarks to Captain Brakowski any more than I am to the rest of the company commanders, but I'm going to start kicking some butts if this carelessness doesn't stop. Are there any questions?"

No one answered.

He continued, seeming to underline each word with strong emphasis. "The second item has to do with some of our personnel falling out with heat prostration. I realize that it is usually our new personnel who are involved and that it is partly due to their not having adjusted yet to the extreme heat over here. When we return to base camp, I want all new personnel to be put on road marches when they come in. And if necessary, we'll reinstitute our daily early morning airborne run for everybody. This hot and humid temperature is here to stay and we will have to learn to live with it. But beyond this, gentlemen, I am confident that the real cause of our heat casualty problem is the failure of our men to consume a proper quantity of water and to take salt tablets when needed. If we run short of either, we will get more. The going will be rough tomorrow due to the dense underbrush. For a time we will be inaccessible to the helicopters. If a man passes out, he will have to be carried, and we can't afford to lose that time.

"Now, one further word. We do not fire tonight at any movement or at any sound. We've already had too much of this sort of thing. It's a hell of a note to find out that at this stage of the war we have killed more of our own men than the Viet Cong have. I know everyone's jumpy and that it's not easy to see things at night, but here is the policy I expect to be followed. On the perimeter, if movement is sighted, rifles and heavy weapons will not be fired—I repeat, will not be fired unless the enemy can be seen clearly. Use your hand grenades if you are not absolutely sure of what you see. That will be all, gentlemen. You're dismissed."

The other officers jumped to their feet and stood at attention until the colonel had left. The group dispersed and the company commanders hurried back to their own companies to conduct staff meetings and pass information along to their platoon leaders and leading NCO's.

After Captain Brakowski's brief staff meeting was over, he asked Goodman to remain behind. "Sergeant Goodman, I have written up a citation for Lieutenant McNeil for his action today in locating our KIA and preventing any more possible casualties by scanning the immediate area for mines. See that this data gets back on the chopper tomorrow morning to our orderly room at base camp. Have one of our clerks back in the area type it up in correct form for my signature when I return."

"Yes, sir. It will be done."

All of a sudden it seemed that the whole world was dark. One moment there had been a busy stir of activity—eating, reading mail, passing out supplies, staking down ponchos for the evening, an officers' planning session. The steady murmur of conversation could be heard from the various groups—there was the clanging of an empty water can, a sharp command given by an NCO, the hacking down of a small tree, the clatter of a distant helicopter beating the air. But, in the next moment it was as though a switch had been flipped and all was dark and silent.

The long night had begun.

# Chapter Four

# *Watch Out for the New Guys*

The heavy rain had stopped. Captain Brakowski and Lieutenant McNeil were bunking down together under their ponchos. Both lay on their air mattresses.

"Say, Bull, you asleep?" Brakowski whispered.

"Naw, Spence, I'm just lying here thinking."

Spence Brakowski, glad Bull was awake, felt a need to talk tonight. A company commander is one of the best jobs in the army. A man has his own command, a good degree of status, and the opportunity to prove himself if he has what it takes. But it's a rough and lonely job. Since it is his command, he sinks or swims with his own decisions. Most battalion commanders let each company commander run his own company. However, this latitude gives him an uncomfortable responsibility. If he makes the right decisions, everything is great. He's the fair-haired boy. But if he fouls up, he's had it. Everyone knows a company commander who has been relieved of his command on the spot. Usually, he was a good man but just made a mistake in judgment at the wrong time and wrong place.

This responsibility was a heavy weight. The realization that his day-by-day decisions affected the lives of one hundred and seventy men was one that didn't wear well. When he put a man on the point, when he sent an element out to recon the area, when he set up his perimeter guard and had men assigned to the various outposts, it could be his signature for someone's death. What right had he to do this? He wasn't God.

"Spence, how do you think things will go tomorrow?" Lieutenant McNeil asked.

"Of course, we can't be sure in love or war, but I don't anticipate any real contact. There will be some snipers and mines, but I think most of the VC are cleared out of this area by now."

"Looks like a pretty rough day on foot though," Bull added. "Judging by the terrain on the map, it looks like we're in for a day of vine swinging."

The captain didn't answer. No point to it. Some days they had it through rice paddies, sloshing knee-deep in water. Other days they untangled a trail for themselves and worked their way through jungle. Tomorrow the menu would say "jungle a la mode."

Spence wondered sometimes if the weight of command was too much to expect of any man. Another thing that really got to him was loneliness. In one of his university courses in the Reserve Officer Training Corps program they discussed the need for a certain distance to exist between the commander and his men. This distance was needed in the military setting where over-familiarity might influence decisions of the commander. As he thought of it, there had been a certain glamour and appeal to it back in those days when status and military pomp and splendor were so prominent in his thinking. But little did he realize how lonely this world of command could be. Though some men might voice a resentment toward a commander's high-handed way, attribute it to his hard-nosed idea of self-importance and determination to get ahead in his career, and refer to him snidely as "chicken brass," nevertheless, they expected him to stand aloof. They counted on the "Old Man" to make the right decision even though they criticized him bitterly. He was the untouchable, father figure—the stability in any situation. So he must stand the pressure from the crowd, think his thoughts alone, and force his judgment as the absolute authority. Sometimes he wished he could kick this leadership binge for awhile and be just like anyone else—blame it all on the brass up above, be carefree, make a mistake now and then, and bitch to the heavens about army chow and anything else that struck him wrong. He'd like to live one whole week without having to make any decisions, just do what he was told, and let the brass worry about the big picture.

Captain Brakowski's thoughts were interrupted by his RTO man, "Sir, the colonel wants you on the phone."

"Ponderosa Papa here."

"Ponderosa Papa, this is Big D. We just received a report that a company-sized movement was noted today directly east of your present location. We're not sure, I repeat, not sure of the reliability of this info., but you had better alert your perimeter guard. Do you have your trip flares in position? Over."

"Yes, sir, we have a good number out. Over."

"Ponderosa Papa, if anything develops, I want to be contacted immediately. In all probability nothing will happen, but we just want to be ready. Over and out."

"Roger and out," Brakowski replied. Then he added, "Bull, you get on the phone and pass the word along to the other platoon leaders. Emphasize that the reliability of this report is not established. This is merely a precautionary alert."

"O.K., sir."

"First Sergeant," Brakowski called, "over here."

"Yes, sir," First Sergeant Goodman answered him quickly. "Be right over, sir." Captain Brakowski relayed the recent message. "Sergeant Goodman, be sure the NCO's are aware of the situation, but be equally sure no one pushes the panic button. We don't want anyone going off half-cocked and firing at shadows. You know the Old Man's policy about no firing until something is actually seen."

"Roger, sir, will do." The first sergeant jumped to his feet and disappeared into the night.

The young commander settled back down on his air mattress, his mind racing through a mental check of items that he might need to consider in view of these developments. It seemed that surely there ought to be something else he should be doing. After wracking his brain for any possible oversights and finding none, he closed his eyes hoping to fall asleep.

Brakowski was the perfect stereotype of a poor little rich boy. Born to great wealth, he had lived in the land of luxury. His great-grandfather had amassed a fortune in steel. This had been passed on down through the family from father to son. When other children were receiving bicycles and cowboy suits for birthday and Christmas presents, Spence and his brothers were given stock in the family business with the expectation that ultimately they would assume their role of leadership in the company and become captains in industry. Spence went along with this belief until he was almost through college, but one day an older brother stopped by to see him. Obviously unhappy in spite of his wealth and position of influence, he begged Spence not to become a part of the machine and trade his soul for "the steel monster." This encounter was a turning point.

In the days following his brother's visit it was as though he surveyed the structure of his soul for the first time. He asked questions—questions that in the past he had refused to entertain. Exactly who was he? What was he? Where was he going? Why? Was he happy? Was he living or just existing? Did he really want to be a steel tycoon or would he rather be a person, honest, free, and alive?

All of a sudden he was no longer Spence Brakowski, son of Mr. Brakowski, steel magnate. He became just Spence Brakowski, private citizen. He liked the feel of it. It was his declaration of independence. For the first time he saw himself as he had been, and it made him sick.

The hard part was yet to come. He knew he had to face the inevitable moment of truth with his father. Indian boys, before they can become braves, have to prove themselves by submitting to certain trials. One is to face a wild animal and bring its hide back as a token of his prowess and manhood. Spence had to face his father. That was to be his trial; his test of manhood.

The scene was unpleasant. He announced that he had volunteered for active duty in the army. At first the older man was very angry. He cursed and called his son a stupid, hardheaded, spoiled brat—an ingrate. Then he was meek and listed all he had done for the boy. When none of these maneuvers produced the expected results, he slumped down in his leather chair, shook his head, and said that maybe the army could make a man out of his son.

Life in the army was the greatest thing that ever happened to him. For the first time he became an adult. When someone called his name, he knew they were referring to Spence Brakowski, Captain, U.S.A., not just the factory president's son. The army had made him an authentic person.

An urgent whisper was heard out of the dark, "Don't shoot, it's me, Private Ellington."

A reply came back, "Twenty-four."

This was the challenge for the night. If a guard was not sure of the identity of the person approaching, he would challenge him by stating two numbers under five. The other would answer the challenge by multiplying these two numbers together.

Ellington responded by whispering, "Eight."

"O.K., come on over."

Ellington crawled over to the hole in the ground where two guards were stationed.

The trench was about three and one-half feet deep and extended just outside the tree line. It had been dug so that it could be entered by crawling in from behind a clump of trees. To its left was an irregular line of trees, and to its right was a partial clearing, and to the front of the position was a field about forty meters wide. The edge of the jungle began again at the edge of this field. Fifty meters to the left and right the two guards could see their flank positions. Their assignment was to be the first line of defense. They were to guard the area immediately in front of them and to form a cross fire if necessary to their left and right flanks.

Some planks from an ammunition crate placed across the two mounds of dirt on each side of the trench formed a partial ceiling. Packing dirt on the planks camouflaged them fairly well. The dugout wouldn't win any beauty contests, but it did afford a little shelter from the weather and a good line of fire across the area.

"Washington, what in the hell are you doing here?" Ellington exclaimed as he recognized one of the soldiers squatting in the hole.

"That's what I'm wondering," the Negro soldier replied. "I don't remember volunteering for nothing."

"Well, I tell you what I'm gonna do for you, soldier," Ellington said. "I'm going to give you something that will help keep you awake."

"What's that?"

"I got some news. Word is being passed around that enemy movement has been seen out here east of you, right in your front yard. The Old Man said not to get all shook, probably nothing will develop, but this is just an alert to give you something to think about tonight."

"Just leave it to us."

"O.K., See you. Sleep tight. Wish I could stay up here with you, but you know how it is, they don't allow cowards up front," Ellington said as he crawled away.

"Say, Washington, is he on the level with us, or do you think he's kidding?" the other soldier asked anxiously.

"Naw, man, he ain't kidding. He wouldn't be crawling out

here in the dark if he didn't have to, you can be sure of that."

Sullivan, the young soldier sitting by the side of SP/4 Washington was extremely nervous. He had arrived in Viet Nam only six days ago—just in time to be placed in his new unit, draw out his gear, and depart on this operation. Of course, talk of past battles, close escapes, and tales of horror were standard topics of conversation around the base camp. The old-timers in the unit got special delight in going into lurid details when talking to the new men. They would always lay it on thick. However, these bull sessions were not needed in order to break in the new men. Usually their first operation illustrated all too well what they could expect for the months ahead, and as morbid as were the war tales enthusiastically presented by the veterans, they were like fairy tales as compared to the shock of the real thing.

Suddenly the crack of an M-16 rifle was heard, followed by a scream of pain.

"Don't shoot, don't shoot, you fool, you've hit me. It's me, Ellington!"

"What is it, Washington? What is it?" Sullivan asked, his weapon clenched tightly in his hands and ready to fire as his eyes fought to pierce the darkness.

"I don't know, but hold it. Don't fire," Washington snapped. "It sounds like one of our own men is hurt."

The message was relayed down the line with one soldier passing it on to another. "Hold your fire, let the medic through. Ellington's been hit."

The voice of the medic was heard, "Don't fire, men, it's me, Peavy. Which way," he called.

"Over here," a voice replied. "Over here, doc."

Several men were talking, but the words were too muffled to be understood. Then the voice of Lieutenant McNeil could be recognized. He was talking over his radio to the company commander. It became apparent that Ellington had been shot in the leg by one of the guards. In a few minutes two men came by carrying Ellington on a stretcher. The doc and Lieutenant McNeil followed behind.

Sullivan called out, "Hey, doc, is that Ellington? How is he?"

The medic answered, "Yea, one of the guards shot him, but he'll be O.K."

"How'd it happen?" Sullivan asked again.

Peavy continued, "I'm not sure, but I think the guard challenged him too softly and fired when he didn't answer."

"You guys knock off that chatter. If you'd do more listening instead of so much talking, this sort of thing wouldn't happen so often. Now watch what you're doing," ordered the lieutenant.

Both Washington and Sullivan settled back down in their trench. The shot and then the scream had put their nerves on edge. That moment of alarm had drained them emotionally. They both sat quietly for a good while, breathing deeply.

Finally Sullivan broke the silence. "This is a hell of a place. How much more time do you have over here, Washington?"

"Only five more, friend, only five more."

"You mean you have only five more days and you go home?" the private asked unbelievingly.

"Naw, not five more days—five more paydays. I go home five months from yesterday," Washington explained. "It doesn't seem so long if you think of it like that."

They had been sitting in their trench talking quietly and feeling some measure of security in their position, when suddenly the sky lighted up. The two men sat there, staring upward. They realized the flimsiness of their own cover when they saw the nakedness of the positions of their other buddies. It had seemed like such a snug spot when they had dug in under the protection of darkness, but now, suddenly exposed to a dazzling light, the little knoll behind which they crouched cast a shadow which seemed to offer scant protection.

"Stay down low," Washington whispered, "somebody's set off a trip flare."

A number of such flares were always put just outside the perimeter of any encampment. They were placed so that one would be tripped off if the enemy attempted a probe. The flare was propelled upward to a designated height and ignited. It gave a very bright light for forty-five to sixty seconds, and if Viet Cong soldiers had penetrated the area, this light made them easy to see. But a flare did not always indicate the presence of Viet Cong. The trip device was so sensitive that it could be set off by some small animal scurrying about in the night, or by a number of things that just happened and were never detected.

At such times you never knew what caused the flare to go off. All the men laid low so as not to be detected, all eyes swept across the area searching for objects or movements during the brief seconds available, all muscles tensed and hearts pounded. The momentary glare could reveal Viet Cong approaching, or it could reveal just mysterious nothingness—the hint of something unknown lurking out of sight.

The flare was burning itself out. As it floated downward, it caused shadows to play tricks. Then, it was dark, but the darkness seemed more intense now.

"Do you see anything? Is that something moving over there?" The new soldier asked.

They waited, but nothing happened.

Finally, Washington said, "Well, guess it was just a little fireworks display for our entertainment. The Old Man probably had it set off to keep us from getting bored. Why don't you go on and get a little sack time, and I'll take the first watch."

"Sleep? Who can sleep in a spot like this? Even if I could go to sleep, how do I know you'd stay awake? And I know I'm not gonna sit up here by myself while you are asleep."

"What's wrong with you?" Washington asked. "Don't you know we're airborne troopers and nobody can scare an airborne trooper? We're hard core, man."

"Okay. Better go out there and tell the VC's how tough we are; they may not know. They may not be able to see these silver, jump-wings on our chests out here in the dark, and shoot at us like they would some leg trooper." The airborne soldier traditionally refers to all non-airborne troops as "legs." It sounds like swearing when it is said with the proper feeling.

"Better get some sleep. You'll need it."

"Okay, Washington, I'll try."

Private Sullivan leaned back against the side of the trench and stretched out as though he were going to sleep. But his eyes stayed open. He was thinking to himself that his buddy was right. He'd have to get some sleep. If he didn't, he might fall asleep later when he was supposed to be on watch. From behind him he heard the faint sound of snoring. It was surprising how sounds carried out here at night. How could anybody in his right mind sleep like that in a place like this?

"Washington, you awake?" he whispered.

"Yeah, why?" came the answer.

"Oh, just checking."

A few minutes passed and all was quiet. Washington looked over at his fellow guard. His eyes were closed. Washington smiled, knowing what the boy was going through. The first several nights in the field are rough, especially when assigned on a guard post.

But not only was he happy that his buddy was able finally to get some sleep, he was relieved. It is always rough to pull guard with a new man. His anxiety had a way of conveying itself to the other man in the trench. If he fell asleep during his watch, which some do, not only would his partner's life be jeopardized, but the lives of all those who depended on his alarm. But worst of all, a scared man was a dangerous man. He could hurt himself and he could hurt others. Most of the old troopers were more apprehensive of the new men walking at their sides than of the Viet Cong. Such men were so jittery they became trigger happy. And a trigger happy soldier with an automatic weapon that can be fired instantly with the slightest pressure became in himself a lethal weapon.

"Washington?"

Washington was startled at the sound of his name and jumped as one does who feels an unexpected tap on his shoulder in the dark. "What do you want?"

"I was just wondering if you had ever seen a real Viet Cong up close," the boy said.

Washington thought for a moment and then replied, "Well I never saw a Viet Cong face to face, but I have seen some who had been killed."

"What do them 'gooks' look like up close, Washington, do they look anything like us?"

"No, they're not like us. They're small and shifty, and with that judo stuff they can kill a man with their bare hands."

"But what do they look like in the face?" the soldier persisted. "Would I recognize one if I saw him out here? We have lots of different nationalities in our army. Suppose a VC crawled up here and said a few words of English. How would we know whether or not he's on our side?"

"Easy. If you pass by a Vietnamese and he shoots at you, he's the enemy. If he don't shoot, then he's on our side."

"Ha, ha," Sullivan said sarcastically, realizing he had been taken in.

"But seriously," Washington continued, "you can't mistake 'em. They got yellow skin, slant eyes, and jet black hair, and—well, you'll know 'em."

"Yeah."

"Sullivan, since you decided not to sleep any while you're over here, why don't I just get my nap now? I'll wake up in a little while and take over the second watch."

"O.K., go on and take a break, but don't start snoring."

Washington crawled over and stretched out lengthwise in their shallow trench. Just as he shut his eyes he felt Sullivan tap him on the shoulder.

"What?"

Sullivan whispered, "If I see anything, I'll tap you like this, and boy if I do, don't fool around, wake up and help me."

"Sure, but don't tap if you don't have to. Say, what time is it?"

"It's just a little after midnight," the private answered.

"What do you say we pull three hour shifts? I'll sleep until zero three hundred hours, you wake me then and I'll take over." Washington fell asleep immediately.

Sullivan sat still and just stared into the distance. From time to time he would scan the tree line in front of him. What a way to earn a living! It seemed as though he had been sitting there for hours, listening and waiting. The boredom would have been painful had he not preferred it over any excitement. The one thing he didn't want tonight was excitement of any kind. He was delighted to be bored. Wonder what time it is? he thought. Staring at his watch in the dark, he saw that it was twelve-fifteen. Time seemed to be frozen.

"Lord, will this night ever pass?" he thought.

Sullivan had never realized how much went on at night before. He had never given any time to just sitting and listening. Night had always just been a time to sleep or to pick up his girl. But tonight for the first time, he was experiencing a part of life he never knew existed.

He looked up at the stars, and it made him feel insignificant to realize that he was just one speck on this whirling planet which in itself was just a very tiny speck compared to the millions of- other worlds scattered throughout space. It meant his little problems weren't really too important after all.

From time to time Sullivan would think he had seen some

movement. Instantly, all of his attention would be drawn toward the questionable object. As his eyes sought to cut through the darkness, he kept his finger on the trigger of his rifle. After awhile, detecting nothing, he would look away in another direction, but in spite of himself, he would cut back for one more glance. As the moments turned into hours, his fear abated somewhat, but he would be immensely relieved to turn the watch over to Washington.

A faint movement caught his attention. He squinted his eyes in order to see better in the dark. Nothing. He started to chalk it up to his imagination and began to shift his attention on down the line, with just a glance or two back just to double check. But something did appear.

"This is no false alarm; something is out there. Could it be a shadow? No, it has moved under the trees out into the field. Could it be one of our men? No, none of our men are out that far. We're the first line of defense. There must be some mistake. This couldn't happen to me."

But, before he could doubt any more, and as he was reaching over to tap his sleeping buddy, it emerged in full sight. Something was out there and it was moving directly toward his position. The darkness had been deceiving and it was much closer than he had realized. The shock of this discovery threw him into panic.

Sullivan's finger closed on the trigger of his automatic rifle. Instantly the silence of the night was broken. The tracer bullets indicated clearly the direction of his fire, and the red glow of the tracers made them look like the red balls of fire shot from a roman candle.

In seconds the weapon of the guard off to his right flank opened up. It fired in the same direction, and then the man to his left began to fire rapidly. The night was full of the red sparks of tracers, and the thud of rounds tearing into trees could be heard. It seemed as though every weapon in the company was now aiming its fire power into the field and tree line.

Washington was awake instantly. "What happened? What do you see?"

His question was not answered because just at that moment several rounds tore into the tree above them.

"Get down," Washington yelled to Sullivan.

When they looked up, they could see tracers from one of their own positions aimed right at them.

A familiar voice called from the rear, "Hold your fire, hold your fire."

Various men picked up the message and yelled, "Knock it off; hold your fire."

One by one weapons ceased to fire until finally everything was quiet again.

"Is anybody hurt?"

This question was relayed from man to man. No casualties were reported.

Of course, the next question was how many casualties had been inflicted on the enemy? Just what size force had attacked? Had they pulled back or were they dug in just waiting to charge again? Was this the unit that had been reported as being in the area? These questions had to be answered and they had to be answered immediately.

A reconnaissance patrol was formed hurriedly. They were instructed as to their mission—probe the area immediately in front in an attempt to size up the situation. A flare was to be sent up, with observers in place to note any casualties or enemy positions. If the flare brought no enemy reaction, the patrol was to proceed. If it made any contact, they were to wait until support artillery could be signaled.

The flare blazed out across the sky and illuminated the field brightly. No bodies were seen. No enemy positions were detected, and no enemy fire came in. The patrol then crawled out into the area. No sound was heard. Slowly they worked inch by inch through the field and disappeared in the darkness.

After a long wait, the men emerged from the darkness and handed their report to the company commander.

"Well, I'll be damned," was his only comment as he walked away.

"What did it say?" a member of the patrol was asked by one of the guards.

He answered, "Enemy casualty report—one Vietnamese water buffalo. Estimated size of enemy unit—one water buffalo."

# Chapter Five

# Have You Taken Any Scalps Yet?

"O.K., everybody up, this ain't no Biltmore Hotel. We don't serve breakfast in bed," Sergeant Stagg called as he moved from man to man.

It was black dark, but the area was coming alive. Small groups of men had gathered here and there, sitting on the ground and heating cans of coffee over small fires. Cans of C-rations were being opened, and men were eating fruit cocktail, stewed beef, hot chocolate, lima beans, or whatever they happened to have picked up at yesterday's distribution of food.

One moment it was night and then the next it was day. With the coming of the morning there was an exhilarating freshness and newness. There was something about the crisp coolness of the early hours that invigorated the spirit and infused the soul with hope. All the gloominess and trepidation of the night was routed by the first rays of sunlight. Another night was behind them. It was good to be alive.

A large hole was dug before pulling out, and the men were directed to throw all their empty cans and trash into it to be burned.

"Police up your area, men," one of the NCO's yelled. "Don't leave nothing out in the open."

"Sir, may I speak to you a second?" Albright asked Lieutenant McNeil.

"Sure, what's on your mind?"

"Sir, I'd like to volunteer to take the point today."

"Albright, I've already let you take it too many times. We've got plenty of new men. It's about time for them to give it a try. You'll get a chance, don't worry," Lieutenant McNeil answered.

"But, sir, I know my job. I want to be up where the action is. That's where I'm needed."

"Now listen, the Old Man has already spoken to me once about letting you ride the point so often. He doesn't think it's good for one man to be up there as much as you have, whether you volunteer or not. I'm going to pass it around. You'll get your crack at it. Is that all?"

"Yes, sir, that's all, sir," Albright replied as he popped a sharp salute and departed.

The companies now formed up and got in position to move out. Captain Brakowski made a final check with his other officers.

"It's the same story as always, gentlemen. Watch out for snipers, mines, and heat casualties. Have your men checked from time to time to see if they're drinking enough water and taking their salt tablets. We've got a long day ahead of us and some rough going until this afternoon. Let's make it as easy on ourselves as possible. There's no point in trying to make it a hardship tour; it'll be bad enough without our cooperation. Remember to keep about a five-meter interval between each man. Don't let 'em bunch up. I want you platoon leaders to stay in contact with me at all times. If you're not sure of your location, let's check before someone gets lost, and if your element is hit, let me know as quickly as possible. Any questions?"

"Sir," Lieutenant McNeil asked, "if we do come under fire, will it be all right to take the offensive and go after them when they start to pull out? I'm tired of taking it on the chin and then letting them get away."

"Absolutely not, Bull. The orders are to neutralize their fire the best you can, to report the situation to the Old Man, and to wait for orders."

"Hell, Spence, I mean, sir," the lieutenant answered, his face flushing. "There's no damn logic in humping it all over these god-forsaken jungles only to have to sit back and wait for orders when once we find 'Charlie.' I say let's go after him and break his neck."

"And what will you do, Lieutenant, when you catch up with 'Charlie' and find that he has drawn you into a trap and has you surrounded? He'll pick off your men one by one and we won't be able to locate your position until it's too late. Do you get the general drag of the situation, Lieutenant?" the captain said, emphasizing the word, *lieutenant*. "Any questions?" he added.

Looking at this scene of robust, idealistic young men gathered in a small circle, you could almost compare it to a college football team in a huddle. They were tense and absorbed in their activity. From their mannerisms and appearance, it would seem more likely for them to break from the huddle and execute a ball play rather than go into the jungle hunting Viet Cong.

Helicopters were flying overhead, making a reconnaissance of the area that would be entered by the troops. Due to the thickness of the jungle, contact with the observation planes was vital. In order to identify their exact location the units exploded smoke bombs periodically, and the colored smoke would work its way upward, sifting through the tangled canopy of trees to give the planes above an exact "fix." The planes would then radio the commander in the jungle his exact location on the map. In this way the units were directed toward their destination.

The long line now began to move. One detachment worked its way into the tree line across the open field nearest to the camp and the other entered about fifty meters down. One by one each man looked to the left and right, darted across the clearing and disappeared into the jungle, being careful to keep the man in front of him in sight at all times. When the last man in the first group crossed the field, an NCO shouted, "All right, on your feet, let's go," and then two other long lines of heavily armed men began the same penetration.

In a short time the camp area was empty, and there was nothing remaining to indicate the recent presence of eight hundred troopers.

It was apparent from the start that this would be a rough day. After entering the tree line, the jungle seemed to close in from all sides. The foliage became a green cover that shut out nearly all the light from above and created a dismal world down below. The jungle was a murky, wet, insect-laden, and hostile world. It was one not made for man and would not tolerate a human intruder for any long period. Here was a domain of death and decay. Foul odors were in the air. Stagnant water lay in every hollow. Under every fallen tree branch were hundreds of insects, and thorny vines waited to latch onto any passerby. These vines, twisting from tree to tree, formed a kind of prison which defied anyone to escape its clutches.

Today the line moved more slowly than usual. It was a constant fight to keep a solid footing. Often a trooper would find himself entangled and would have to back up and work free. Unexpectedly, another man would trip and fall.

"Ouch," a trooper muttered under his breath as he rubbed a welt on his cheek. "I don't know why these damn mosquitoes always pick on me."

Mosquitoes infested this damp dark world, and in moments a man could be covered with bites. Everyone carried plastic bottles of mosquito repellent in his pocket and kept arms, neck, and face coated. Without thinking, however, a man would forget and rub an arm across his face and grimace as the repellent burned, and smarted lips and eyes.

"Hold up," a voice up front directed.

"Hold up." The order was echoed by first one man and then another down the line.

Most of the men sat down, but a few remained standing, surmising that the break would be too short to sit down and then have to get right up again. But just as the last few holdouts gave up and sat down—with seventy pounds of gear on their backs—the order was shouted, "O.K., saddle up. Let's move out."

"You might know it," a soldier groaned. "As soon as I get down, it's time to get up."

The line was on the move again.

"There's a creek up ahead. Take it careful," someone said.

Splashes were heard as the men up forward waded across. The creek was not very deep, but the men dreaded to walk through it. As they crossed the stagnant pool, they could feel the water rising until it was waist high.

"Keep your weapons out of that crud," Sergeant Stagg called. "O.K., keep moving back there, don't stretch the column out so far. Catch up, pay attention."

The next thing that came into view was a long ditch. It was about twenty-five meters deep, dipping almost straight down. When I got to the edge, I saw two men down in the ditch giving first aid to a third soldier.

"Medic," one of them called. "Hold up, come back, we've got a man with a hurt leg here."

In a few minutes Private Peavy came jogging down the path asking, "Who called for the medic?"

"Down there in the ditch."

"How does it feel?" the medic asked, bending over the man.

"It hurts right there. Take it easy, doc. I can't walk on it, doc. I think I twisted it when I fell."

Private Peavy wrapped a heavy bandage tightly around his patient's leg. "We're gonna have to carry him. Get me something so we can improvise a stretcher."

As the men hacked away at tree branches, Lieutenant McNeil came hurrying down the line.

"What's wrong?" he asked.

The soldier on the ground explained.

"Oh, no, Jimmerson! Not you again. You're gonna have to learn to watch what you're doing. You're just a walking accident looking for a place to happen."

Some of the men standing nearby laughed. Jimmerson had a record of such mishaps. He was never hurt seriously, but he always needed a little special treatment. At first there had been a suspicion that the man was goldbricking. But his list of minor mishaps multiplied. After awhile it was obvious that he was accident-prone.

"I couldn't help it, sir," the enlisted man pleaded. "It's just one of those things."

"I know, I know, don't say anything else, Jimmerson. Those vines stayed right in their places when the other men went by, but when they saw you coming, they recognized you and thought they'd have some fun, right?"

Before the soldier could answer, the medic said, "Sir, he won't be able to walk; he's got a lot of swelling in his ankle. We'll have to carry him until we can evacuate him back to base camp. We're improvising a stretcher now."

"I ought to make him crawl along behind us. Jimmerson, I ought to give you an article 15, but I can't figure whether to give it to you for self-inflicted accidents or for incompetence."

The two men standing alongside roared with laughter.

"Knock it off. What do you think this is, a side show? You two men pick up each end of the stretcher and laugh as you lug it all day. No helicopter will be able to set down and we won't come to any clearing until a couple of hours after lunch. Looks like you really have a fun day lined up for yourselves, doesn't it," McNeil ordered sarcastically as he looked down at the men in the ditch.

As Lieutenant McNeil pivoted around to leave, his foot hit a loose rock, causing him to trip, and the slipping clay on the side of the deep gulley upended the officer and plunged him down-

ward into the ditch toward the patient and the two other
soldiers. In a moment he was lying at the feet of the soldier, his
uniform wet with mud, his face splashed with dirt, and his
helmet in a puddle of water. Sprawled helpless in the filth was
the gung-ho, swaggering McNeil—high-stepping, hard-nosed officer who found imperfection repulsive and any offender intoler-
able.

No one moved or spoke. No expression of amusement showed
on the faces of the men. The blood vessels in his neck began to
enlarge and his face reddened. This was a familiar warning of a
storm about to break. All eyes shifted in other directions; no one
wanted to meet his stare. But the storm subsided, and he rose
to his feet, wiped off the mud, picked up his helmet, and started
up the side of the gulley.

Along the trail leading toward the ditch was another group of
men. Sergeant Stagg was with them. As the first man inched
down the steep side, the sergeant yelled, "Be careful now, or
some damn fool is gonna slide right down on his face." Just as the
last word left his lips, he saw Lieutenant McNeil. The sergeant's
eyes traveled from the lieutenant's, down his muddy body, and
back up again. The words "damn fool" seemed to hang suspended
in the air. For one of the few times in his life he was speechless.
The silence only made it worse.

Quick thinking solved the problem. With all the confidence in
the world he uttered the standard airborne greeting, "All the
way, sir."

This was the perfect phrase that saved the day.

Lieutenant McNeil gave the traditional answer, "Airborne,
Sergeant," and the matter was closed.

Finally all the men crossed the ravine. As they plodded along,
water squirted from the ventilation holes in their jungle boots at
each step. Their thick socks were saturated; clothing was soaked
with perspiration and swamp water in about equal degrees.

Each man followed the man in front. The officers and key
noncommissioned officers had been briefed on the mission for
the day and had an understanding of the big picture. But
"Private Joe Blow" just followed the fellow in front of him. He
didn't know anything about the overall picture and very little
about any one aspect of it. None of it made much sense to him
anyway. He knew what his particular job was and he knew it

well. And when the time came for him to do his stuff, he would be a giant—one of the best fighting men in the world, the best trained and the best informed. All of the rigid and expensive training of the past would be focused in his every movement. He would be a professional, deadly and telling in his impact. But, now, as he plodded along, following the man in front of him, he was just "Private Joe Blow." He couldn't know less and couldn't care less. Someone told him he wasn't paid to think, just to take orders. But things got confusing for him after awhile, and the days got long. He didn't know which way the line was moving, where it was going, what was expected when it got there. He simply knew what he overheard the officers say, what the sergeants repeated, or what some other G.I. gave as his opinion. What private would ask some officer to give him a briefing on the operational plans? Sometimes he felt that if he knew more about what was happening it would make more sense and have more logic than when he just did what he was told and followed the man in front.

He saw that the men up the line were stopping so he prepared to sit down again. They might be here for only several seconds or it might be for two hours. Why fight it? He'd just lie down every opportunity he had. So he stretched out on the grass, put his helmet under his head for a pillow, and closed his eyes.

Jimmy and I were with this group.

"Sir, you gonna have a religious service out here today? It's been quite a while since we had one."

"I'd like to, Jimmy, but I don't think we'll have the opportunity. We'll be on the move most of today, anyway. When we get back to base camp tomorrow, we can line up a service."

Specialist-four Albright was leaning against a tree nearby. "Chaplain, have you gotten any scalps yet?"

"What do you mean, Alex?"

"I mean, Chaplain, have you won any souls yet today?"

The question stung. It was not so much what he said but the ridiculing insinuation. I said, "Come on, Alex, you know that's too big an order for any man. God has to handle jobs like that."

"If you get this outfit to march through those pearly gates, Chaplain, it will probably take all you and the Man upstairs can do together. In fact, it might even help your case to have a medium-sized miracle thrown in."

"Son, I have a feeling that most of us aren't nearly as bad as we'd like each other to think."

I had felt drawn to Alexander Albright from the time of our first meeting. He was clean-cut boy, highly intelligent and a superb conversationalist. But perhaps more than his general attractiveness, the paradox he presented interested me.

It is certainly natural for young men to test their limits with family or society or with existing authority. Ministers are accustomed to individuals attempting to shock them by their unconventional views or daring treatment of the customary moral concepts. But Albright didn't fit this mold of youthful rebellion. The bite in his statements came from down deep in his soul. His barbed comments were measured and shrewdly delivered.

Although Albright was never disrespectful, it was with the precision of a surgeon that he pricked me with verbal scalpels. It was a declared war from the first, but clothed in the sort of propriety with which no one could find fault.

Alex attended chapel regularly. Arriving late, he always sat in the back, and left early. When I conducted services in the field, he could never be found among the small number sitting on the ground participating, but he could always be seen standing nearby.

At first, his antagonism shocked me. Then the shock turned to surprise when the subversion continued for no apparent reason. If I had been the sort of minister who flaunted his religious views before his flock and goaded them into conformity, I could have understood his behavior, but such was far from the case. From being shocked and then surprised, my attitude changed into one that was simply provoked. It wouldn't have been so bad if the man had singled me out privately and barraged me with his arguments, but his usual approach was to engage me in the presence of several other men. He would ask a question that couldn't possibly be discussed adequately in the time available, but which if left undiscussed would imply the truth of his argument.

I wanted to understand Albright and was willing to lay myself open to his charges, hoping that I would hear something that would indicate the source of his bitterness. There was some hurt, some disillusionment, some injury that had wounded this man deeply and was now causing him to strike out wildly. But I couldn't ask him. This would slam the door shut forever. I would have to wait until he wanted to tell me.

A flurry of rifle shots sounded in the distance. All conversation stopped. Each unit was checked to see if it had made any contact with the enemy. No contact had been made.

Lieutenant McNeil ran to Captain Brakowski, "Sir, why don't I take a detail of men and check this out. It sounds like it may be signals. If so, we need to break this thing up."

"On the other hand, Bull, the VC may be trying to draw some of us out and get us piecemeal. But we've got to check it out."

"Sir, I'll take a chance. Let me check it out."

"I'll have to brief the Old Man first. Meantime you assemble a detail of about eight or ten men."

"Roger, sir," the lieutenant answered.

Captain Brakowski contacted the colonel and gave him a rundown on the situation. He asked for permission to send out a patrol to check the source of the firing. The battalion commander agreed, but emphasized that the men were to proceed with extreme caution. They were to report back in at regular intervals and under no circumstances engage the enemy without first clearing with H.Q.

"Lieutenant McNeil, do you have your men picked out yet? Over here when you do," the captain called.

"Just a second, sir, be right there."

Lieutenant McNeil motioned for Sergeant Stagg.

"Sergeant, I want you to go with me to check this out. Pick out nine good men to go with us."

Albright overheard the lieutenant and he rushed over to the sergeant saying, "Sergeant Stagg, count me in. I want to go."

"Never pass up a chance, do you, Albright? All right, get set to move out in ten minutes. If you want action so bad, I can accommodate you." "Hey, Washington, you there, the Old Man wants some volunteers to go out on a patrol. Snap it up. We leave in ten minutes."

"Did you say volunteers, Sarge? I didn't raise my hand; I was just scratching my head," Washington kidded. He added, "I'll sure go right out and find you some volunteers right now if you like, Sarge. How many do you need?"

"Your concern gets me right here, Washington, but I hate to put an old fellow like you to all that trouble. I'll just let you go along so you won't have to look for anyone else. Form up over there."

The sergeant moved on down the line. Some of the men who overheard the nature of this mission faded quietly into the scenery and found something to do elsewhere as they saw the NCO approaching. Sergeant Stagg crept around a clump of bushes and waited until two troopers ran right into him.

"Well, good morning, gentlemen," the sergeant said. "Fancy meeting you here. And just when I was looking for two men to go on a little picnic with me. All right," his voice raised in volume, "prepare to move out in ten minutes. Form up over there by the lieutenant."

The sergeant then walked over to three men who were sitting on the ground talking. One of the men called, "Say, Sarge, if you can use any more on the patrol, Stenson and I would like to go."

"Good, get ready to go. We'll leave from over there in a couple of minutes."

The men jumped to their feet and walked over to the other members of the patrol. "We'll see you, doc," one of them said to Private Peavy.

Sergeant Stagg looked at Peavy and grunted, "You might as well come along, too."

"Come along where, Sergeant?"

"Well, Peavy, it won't be no Easter egg hunt, you can be sure of that."

Shorty Peavy, still confused as to which detail he was being assigned, walked over to the group of men gathered nearby.

"Wonder what kind of dirty work we have to do this time," he thought. "Wouldn't be surprised if we didn't have to clear out some of that undergrowth. Man, you name it, and if it's called work, they look for Peavy."

"You mean there's a medic going with us," Washington exclaimed as Peavy walked up. "Nothing against you, Shorty, but medics always spell trouble."

"What do you mean, Washington, is this supposed to be some kind of patrol?" Private Peavy inquired.

Washington told him that they were going out to locate the source of the shots which had just been fired. It could develop into a hot affair. Although he had overhead that they were not supposed to attempt any direct contact with the enemy, all the men knew that Lieutenant McNeil would not pass up that kind of an opportunity. It was common knowledge that the lieutenant was out to make a name for himself. The rumor was that he had his eye on the Silver Star and would take any risk to get it. And that meant the men with him took the same risk.

"I'll be damned if I'm going out on any patrol," Peavy indignantly muttered. "I'm a medic, not a rifleman. Sergeant Stagg, could I see you a minute?" he asked, going over to where the sergeant was fastening on his gear.

"Later, later, can't you see I'm busy, soldier?"

Peavy continued anyway, "Sergeant Stagg, is it true this patrol is going out to find who fired those shots?"

"Oh, I'm sorry the Old Man neglected to give you a private briefing on the situation, Peavy, seeing that you ain't no run of the mill soldier like the rest of us."

"All I want to know, sir, is are we. . . ."

"Don't call me sir, soldier, I work for a living."

"All right, all right, Sergeant. I'm just asking you straight—are you asking me to go out on a patrol that's supposed to check out a possible enemy location?"

"No, Private, I ain't. I don't ask privates anything. I'm telling you to shut your big mouth and get ready to move out."

For a moment Peavy was so angry that he could not speak. He tried to wait until he could form his words properly, but his temper rushed him headlong into an argument.

"Damn it, Sergeant, you know a medic is not supposed to be sent out on patrols like this. My job is to be ready to help the men, not to be out in the bush as a rifleman."

"Don't tell me what your job is, Private. Your job is to do what I say and I say you're going. You're not scared are you, Shorty?"

"It's not a matter of being afraid, Sergeant, I shouldn't be going out on this patrol and you know it. What are you . . .?"

The sergeant interrupted, "Well, well, so your real color is finally showing itself and it's a bright yellow. I've heard that you were chicken and I've been waiting to hear you cackle."

Peavy clenched his fists until his knuckles turned white. He was on the verge of taking a swing at Stagg when a soldier ran up.

"Sarge, Lieutenant McNeil said to tell you to bring the detail over; he's ready to move out."

"All right, Medic. Some of the other 'sisters' can handle the bandages while you're gone. Get your weapon and get over there." The sergeant turned away without looking back.

Private Peavy walked slowly over to the patrol. He was trembling, partly out of the anger aroused in him by Sergeant Stagg and partly out of apprehension for the activity into which he had been ordered. He knew that as a medic he should not be sent on such a mission. It was not that he was afraid—no one's job was more dangerous than the medic's. Everyone knew that. He must often go in under fire to pull men out. This was bad enough, but it couldn't be helped. But this situation was stupid. Over and above the necessary risks of the medic, he had to serve as a rifleman, just because of the arrogance of Sergeant Stagg.

The officer in charge of the patrol walked over and told the men to move out. Peavy was standing toward the rear. The men in front started to move out. When it came his time to go, he stood still. It wasn't so much that he planned to remain behind; it was just that at first he didn't step forward. As the distance between himself and the man in front of him lengthened, he expected to move out and catch up. But he didn't. Soon the line of men disappeared into the trees and he still stood in place. No one had noticed. For the first time, the young soldier realized that he was staying behind.

As casually as he could manage, he sat down by a tree, slid down on his back and closed his eyes. It was too late now to join the men even if he wanted to, so there was no need worrying about it. All he wanted to do was live. What was so wrong about that? He was no hero, but he was no coward either. One thing was certain, he would do his job, but that was all. He just wanted to live until it was all over.

Private Peavy rolled on his side. It was very comfortable there in the cool shade, and before very long he was asleep.

# Chapter Six

## *Listen to My Sermon, Chappie*

Lieutenant McNeil and his detail moved cautiously through the jungle. At intervals the officer ordered three of his men forward. They would fan out in front, and if nothing was sighted, the others would be signalled to come up. By this time they knew they must be near the approximate area where the shots had been fired shortly before. Every fifty or hundred meters the lieutenant radioed back to Captain Brakowski.

Things were quiet, too quiet. No sound was heard except the rustling of leaves in the trees and the scuffling of the men's boots. Now and then a twig would snap under a man's foot, and the little column would wait, then move on cautiously.

Albright was probing out to the left. He was pushing ahead too far and too fast, and from time to time he was completely out of sight. Sergeant Stagg didn't like this. "The damn fool is taking too many chances."

"Go get him, Sergeant," McNeil said. "I want to be able to see every man at all times. When the jungle thins out, the men can spread farther apart. Tell them that any time they can't see me, they're too far out."

The sergeant hurried forward. He was afraid to call out since the sound might alert the Viet Cong. On the other hand, if he accidently slipped up on Albright, he might find himself looking down the muzzle of an M-16 rifle. So, Stagg made his way through the underbrush very cautiously, muttering to himself.

Suddenly a twig snapped behind him. Combat wise as was this experienced veteran, he had seen nothing. If anything was around, he ordinarily could sense it. The sound was behind him. He whirled around, every nerve tense.

Alexander Albright was crouching in a clump of bushes directly behind the sergeant. He had decided to crawl into this temporary camouflage in order to observe any possible movement around him. In a few moments he was startled by a soldier who almost touched him as he walked past. Albright had been giving his full attention to the forward area, so when the man approached from the rear, he was caught by surprise. He tightened his grip on his weapon and came face to face with the sergeant. For a moment they stood facing each other. It was a tense situation.

Without a word the two men, after the initial shock of indecision, simply sat down. Each experienced a feeling of weakness, as though the strength had been drained from their bodies.

Sergeant Stagg spoke first, "Albright, I ought to . . ." and his voice faded out.

"I know, Sergeant. I'm sorry. I almost killed you. One second more and I would have blown your head off."

Sergeant Stagg could usually bombard the atmosphere with choice words of profanity, but now he was short on words. His face was pale. It was frightening to realize that he had brushed against death. But what really terrified him was that as he whirled around he had grasped a hand grenade and partially pulled the pin. In another split second he would have tossed it into the bushes at the figure crouching there. There wouldn't have been enough left to identify.

"Let's go back," the sergeant said.

They walked back quietly.

"Albright, you were out too far. Lieutenant McNeil said never to get out of his sight. I'll take over awhile now. Be more careful next time."

"O.K."

Both men knew what had almost happened. Neither wanted to talk about it.

Washington called back, "Lieutenant McNeil, Lieutenant McNeil."

"What is it, Washington?" Stagg whispered as he edged over toward him.

"Tunnels over here."

Half hidden in the heavy jungle growth was the mouth of a tunnel.

Lieutenant McNeil said quickly, "Radio the Old Man what we've found and tell him we're checking them out."

Holding his M-16 rifle, he edged toward the hole and peered down into it, but could detect nothing.

"Cover me," he whispered and jumped down into the tunnel.

We held our breath. Nothing happened. Several minutes passed.

"Lieutenant McNeil," one of the men called.

"Just a minute, I'll be up in a minute." And sure enough, he popped out of the tunnel.

"Do any of you have a flashlight? There may be more of 'em. I want to go in and see where they lead."

"Sir," the radioman interrupted, "I've gotten in contact with Captain Brakowski, and he wants to talk to you. I told him you were in a tunnel and he got pretty upset. He wants you to call him the minute you get out."

"All right, let's move on," the lieutenant directed.

"Sir, aren't you going to return the captain's call?"

"Private, I'll tell you when I want to call. I'll call when I have more to report. Let's move on."

They found several other tunnels. "RTO, tell the captain we've found a series of tunnels and we're going in to check them out. Let's go."

The men looked at each other in disbelief and then followed the officer. Albright darted across the clearing and disappeared into another hole.

"That's downright reckless if you ask me," one of the soldiers blurted out.

"Yeah," said another, "There's a difference between being brave and just crazy. I don't care if Lieutenant McNeil *is* an officer, I say he's a fool."

"Knock the chatter off, you guys," Sergeant Stagg ordered. "Let's check these tunnels out."

"O.K., O.K., Sergeant, but I'm not gonna commit suicide. I'm gonna do a little poking around first before I go sticking my head down into any hole in the ground. I may not be any hero, but I ain't no fool, neither."

Some of the tunnels were just large enough for a man to crawl into on hands and knees. They would be straight for about twenty-five meters, make a turn for ten or fifteen meters, and come out inside a trench. The Viet Cong made good use of these tunnels. They would crouch in a trench waiting for an American soldier to approach. The VC would take sure aim, fire, dive into a tunnel and crawl *under* the Americans toward their rear. Ten or fifteen yards behind them would be another trench, out of which the Viet Cong would pop up and fire on them again. Many of our soldiers were killed this way.

The lieutenant called for Sergeant Stagg. As the sergeant climbed down into the tunnel, he couldn't believe his eyes. He was in an area as large as a living room, packed with supplies of all kinds.

"What do you think about this?"

"Never seen anything like it, sir. Sir, look over here."

Apparently families of the Viet Cong had been living here. Articles of clothing and children's schoolbooks were lying around. There was a large cache of rice in one corner. There was no telling how long it had been stored there. The Viet Cong could live for a long time on such a supply.

A large Communist flag hung on the wall. One of the men took it down, folded it, and prepared to put it in his pocket as a prized souvenir.

"Leave it alone, soldier," the officer snapped. "Don't you know they mine this stuff? Sergeant, get the word out that there will be no souvenir taking until we have everything checked out for mines and until our intelligence has had a chance to look everything over."

"Yes, sir."

"Well, I'll be damned. Do you see what I see?" a trooper called as he pointed to a stack of supplies.

Stamped on the sack in English were the words, "Presented by the people of the United States of America." Underneath was a picture of two hands clasped in a gesture of friendship.

"So here's where our gifts to the Vietnamese people end up."

Bunched up in a stack were several American rifles, as well as what appeared to be Chinese and Soviet rifles. A number of Claymore mines lay on the ground.

"Men, you know what this means," McNeil said. "They would have taken all this stuff with them if they had expected us, or if they had had time. The presence of this equipment means one of two things. Either they are around here watching us right now or they had to move out in a hurry. We can't take any chances. Keep your eyes open. They won't give this stuff up without a fight if they're still here."

"Sir, Captain Brakowski is on the phone and wants to talk to you."

Before the lieutenant could say a word, the captain broke in, "What do you mean going into those tunnels without first contacting me? You knew better than that. Now what is the situation?"

"Sir, we've found a series of tunnels and are checking them out. I thought you would want something to tell the Old Man so I decided I would get you something. I think we've found a training center of some kind. There are a number of weapons and documents, along with a large amount of rice and other stuff. I recommend that we move in here and go over the area thoroughly."

Gruffly, Captain Brakowski cut in. "Stay where you are and wait for further instructions. Do you understand? Repeat, proceed no further until I contact you. Over and out."

Quickly the captain briefed the battalion commander on the situation. It sounded far too good to pass up, so the colonel decided to send one company into the area, with the other companies flanking in case a Viet Cong unit was still around. Brakowski's company was selected, so his troops moved forward.

Lieutenant McNeil was annoyed by the captain's radio conversation. He was not the kind to back down, but he knew you didn't fight your company commander. However, he detested what he called the "chicken" approach to everything. He was sick and tired of sending his men out to die day after day and then being told to play it safe and let things drag on and on. If he was in charge, he would go after the Viet Cong and give them no rest. Oriental people understood just one thing—force. They were born hungry and afraid. When they saw weakness in a person, they lost respect for him and took advantage of it.

"Sir, look over here," a trooper called. Under a straw mattress was a second tunnel, with steps leading downward.

"Well, what d'you know," Washington chuckled, "a two-story tunnel. They're sure getting fancy. Pretty soon these Viet Cong are gonna start putting in elevators."

"Sir, we'll check it out," Albright said as he and another man headed for the tunnel.

"Be careful. Go slow," the sergeant advised. "Watch your step; you never know."

The two soldiers descended into a room smaller than the one above but large enough for them to stand upright. There was another tunnel just large enough for one man leading out from this one. The young private crawled in first and Albright followed. The tunnel was dark and led away from the area.

Meanwhile Washington climbed down into the lower room and started into the new tunnel. "It sure is dark in here. Where are you?" he called out.

"Is that you, Washington?" Albright yelled back.

"I'm about fifteen meters inside the tunnel and Stenson is about ten meters in front of me. Say, Stenson, how's it going?"

"Everything's O.K. so far, Alex. I think I see an opening up ahead."

"Well, hold it up until I get there, and we'll go out together."

A few seconds later Stenson called back, "It's an opening all right. Looks like it's in a trench. I'll climb out to see what things look like top side."

As Albright reached the opening, he looked up and saw Stenson climb the wall of the trench and stand on the edge.

"Everything looks quiet enough," Stenson said. His words were interrupted by a loud crack. It was the sound of a Viet Cong rifle. Stenson tumbled downward.

"Watch out, Stenson, you're right on top of me." Albright had been pushed face down into the clay bottom of the trench. "Damn it, get up, you're all over me." By this time he had worked partially free from the weight of the trooper who had fallen on him. He twisted Stenson around and came face to face with his buddy. He was dead, very dead—no doubt about it. His only wound was a small hole in the forehead. His eyes were still open, but there was no life in them.

"Good Lord," Albright said when he was able to speak.

The weight of his companion still had him pinned down. Finally, he rolled him over and was free. Half stunned, Albright stood up.

Another crack sounded as suddenly and unexpectedly as the first one. Albright was knocked to the ground and fell across Stenson's body. He was aware that he could not see and that he had a terrible throbbing in his head. His first thought was, "My God, that sniper is still out there. I'm a goner if he moves in now. I've got to do something."

At that moment Washington crawled from the tunnel. He had heard the two cracks vaguely and moved quickly toward his friends. The first sight to greet him was his two fallen comrades. He froze, and his mouth dropped open. This was the kind of thing you didn't believe even when you saw it. Both men were covered with blood.

"What am I gonna do? What am I gonna do? What am I gonna do?" Washington repeated over and over. "Oh Lord, help me, I've got to do something," he prayed. He thought both of his buddies were dead.

"Washington, is that you?" Albright asked.

"Alex, Alex, yes, this is Washington. Say something else, man."

Albright sat up and held his hands to his head. "Am I hit bad, Washington?"

"You got blood all over, but I can't see no cuts."

"We'd better get back into the tunnel, Washington, that sniper is still out there. I'll go in first and pull Stenson in behind me. You cover us with your rifle. But, buddy, be sure you don't let him get you in his sights."

Albright backed into the mouth of the tunnel. He grasped the lifeless body under its arms and pulled it along slowly. Washington sat alert with his weapon pointed upward. After the other two had disappeared into the darkness, Washington followed.

But it was too much for Albright. He wasn't strong enough. "Just stay there, Washington, and let me get out first. I'm going to have to let someone take over for me."

He wormed his way back into the upper room. The sergeant helped him up, asking, "What happened out there? Are you all right?"

"I'm okay. I think he musta just scraped my helmet. There's a sniper out there, and he got Stenson right between the eyes. He's still in the tunnel. Somebody has got to pull him out. Washington is covering for us."

Quickly, a soldier jumped into the tunnel and returned a few moments later with Stenson's body. Washington followed.

The body was wrapped in a poncho. Lieutenant McNeil examined Albright's head. He would have a welt across his face for a few days, but he was alive. If he had been standing one inch to the right, he would be wrapped in a poncho too.

"Let's get that sniper," Sergeant Stagg snapped. "You go around that way, you go around there, and I'll head straight through. Keep low and protect yourself. When one of us draws fire, we'll know where he is. Move out."

The three men edged forward slowly. They stayed low and kept under cover. Nothing happened.

The sergeant yelled, "I'll fire several rounds into the tree line and hope to flush him out. Keep your eyes open. We've got to pinpoint him the first time he fires or some of us could get hurt."

The NCO checked his rifle to see if it was on automatic. He pulled the trigger and his weapon trembled in his grasp as it blasted the tree limbs. Limbs fell and leaves floated downward. And then there was silence. They waited.

"All right," the sergeant ordered. "Let's move forward." He stood up and pointed to a large tree nearby. Zing! He didn't make it to the tree, but fell to the ground and rolled toward better cover.

One of the other soldiers leaped to his feet and shouted, "The sergeant's been hit."

"Stay down, you fool," Stagg called. "He just winged me in the leg. Stay under cover. I think that shot came from ground level, not from up in the trees. At any rate we . . ."

"I'm not sure," the other soldier interrupted, "but I think I saw movement in the trench over there just after you were hit. I am going to toss a grenade in that direction. Everybody stay low."

He took a grenade from his belt, determined the point he wanted to hit, pulled the pin, and heaved it. Before it landed he was face down on the ground. A loud boom was heard as the grenade hit the ground and exploded. Dirt was thrown into the air and covered the nearby area with dust.

Sergeant Stagg moved forward on his belly, crawled several meters, waited, and then crawled again. Finally he made it to within a few yards of where the grenade had landed. With painful caution he crept up to the trench and looked in. No one moved.

"Well, I'll be damned," Stagg finally said. "We got us a 'gook.'"

"I got me one, I got me one," Martin exclaimed exuberantly. He ran a few steps back toward the others and said proudly, "Lieutenant McNeil, I got me one."

"Martin, stay down, he just may have a buddy out there who wants to get him a G.I.," the lieutenant instructed the young soldier.

"Yes, sir, Lieutenant," he answered, but he ran back in an upright position toward the sergeant.

"You idiot," Sergeant Stagg bellowed. "Don't run back out here like you're going to the county fair. Get down, boy, before you are shot down."

The private bent low, "Yes, Sergeant." He moved up toward the trench to see his game.

Young Martin looked over into the trench. There on the ground was a corpse that resembled a body only to a small degree. It was small, wore sandals, and was clad in black pajamas that were caked with dust. When Martin saw the face of the dead Viet Cong soldier, his face paled and he felt sick.

The point man of the lead platoon came into view. Soon the entire company moved into the area. Captain Brakowski appeared and walked over to Lieutenant McNeil. "What was all the firing about, Bull?"

"Spence, we had a sniper who was holed up in one of the trenches. He got Stenson with his first shot and then creased Albright and nicked Stagg in the leg. But we got him. He's over in that trench," McNeil answered as he pointed to where the dead Viet Cong lay.

"Right. Good work," Brakowski answered. "Search the Viet Cong body for any information that may be significant. Conserve any papers that may be of any intelligence use." He continued, "Sergeant Goodman, be sure we get a perimeter guard set up before we do anything else. I don't want us getting hit while we search this area. Also be sure that the patrols we send out stay in close contact with us, and get the mortars set up in case we need a little extra support."

The company commander then contacted the colonel and briefed him on the situation of the moment.

The patrols started to call back, and each one indicated the presence of trenches and tunnels—but no Viet Cong. A great deal of rice was located and a number of documents. When he received this information, the colonel decided to move the rest of the battalion into the general area and set up camp for the night. This would give the men time to gather up every particle of material that might be of use, burn the rice, and do as much damage as possible to the tunnels. The next morning the unit would move to a designated area for the lift back to base camp.

Albright had been looking for the medic in order to ask him to take a look at his head. The sergeant overheard him ask another trooper where he was.

Stagg sounded off, "Say, I forgot all about Peavy! Where's he been? He's supposed to have been with us on the patrol, but I haven't seen him at all. Peavy, front and center!"

Peavy answered sheepishly.

"You want me, Sarge? What's wrong with your leg? What happened?"

"Peavy, where have you been? If you'd been where you were supposed to, you would have known what happened. Peavy, did you go out with the patrol like I told you to?"

Shorty knelt and opened his medic's bag to dress the sergeant's leg wound.

Sergeant Stagg raised his voice. "Listen, boy, answer my question, did you go out with the patrol like I told you?"

"No, Sarge, I didn't," Shorty answered meekly, trying to avoid meeting the sergeant's eye.

"What? You didn't? And why not? Answer me!" Peavy knew this was not the time to say much. Sergeant Stagg was not easy to talk to at any time, and when he felt a direct order had been disobeyed, he became wild. Also the wound had probably shaken him up and put him under additional strain. But there was no way out now. The sergeant was determined not to let him avoid the matter and was pushing for an answer.

"It's hard to explain, Sergeant. I meant to come, but before I knew what was happening the patrol had gone."

The hair on the sergeant's neck bristled. His voice rose in volume. He pawed at the ground with his fist. "Like hell you intended to go on patrol. You don't take me for a fool, do you? I'll tell you what you did—you just plain refused to follow orders. You were so yellow you just decided to let somebody else do the dirty work for you and didn't think I'd ever know."

This tirade was too much for Shorty. He shook his fist in the sergeant's face and shouted, "You're a bigmouthed liar and if you don't like it, do something about it."

There was a pause.

"All right, kid, you asked for it and I'm gonna give it to you. If I didn't have this bad leg, I'd take you out in the woods and turn you every way but loose. I may do it yet. But right now,

I'm gonna cook your goose in another way. When we get back to base camp, I'm going to press charges against you for insubordination, failure to carry out a direct order, and disrespect to a noncommissioned officer. Report to me tomorrow at base camp. Until then stay out of my sight. Now move out, yellow belly."

Peavy stood with fists clenched. The atmosphere was heavy with tension.

Fortunately, I walked into the area at that moment. Seeing me was enough to cool things off. Peavy controlled himself with an effort.

"Hello, Peavy, Sergeant Stagg. How is it going?"

The spell was broken. Private Peavy's eyes shifted from the sergeant to me.

"Fine, Chaplain Grayson, it's good to see you, sir. When will the next religious service be?"

"I think I'll have services this evening, Shorty. Hope you can make it."

I spotted the sergeant's leg wound and squatted down beside him. As we talked, Private Peavy excused himself and left.

The area around us was busy as an ant hill, with lines of soldiers coming and going in all directions. The tunnels were investigated, enemy weapons, ammunition, and papers were gathered up, and a clearing was prepared for the incoming choppers.

After the dead Viet Cong had been checked for any valuable papers or maps, two men were directed to take shovels and bury the body in the trench. As they threw on shovel after shovel of dirt, they were silent. The body had not been mistreated, but it just didn't seem right to simply throw dirt on it like that. They had no love for the dead VC, and they realized he had just killed one of their buddies and would have killed more if possible, but still he was a *person*. He was a soldier and probably hadn't liked all this hell any more than they did.

"Hey, trooper," another soldier called, "put this billfold back on the body before you finish burying it. We have all the information we need."

One of the men took the billfold. There were several photographs inside. The first was of a smiling, dark-haired young woman.

"Must be his wife. Kinda pretty," he thought.

The next was of the same girl, this time with a man by her side, undoubtedly the dead VC. They looked peaceful and happy.

"I don't guess they ever dreamed when this was taken that an American G.I. would be looking at it."

And then there was a picture of them both. The girl was holding a baby.

"My God, I can't look at it any more." He gently pushed the wallet into the chest pocket of the Viet Cong's uniform and under his breath said quietly, "I'm sorry."

And very soon the job was completed.

The two men had gone when I walked over and stood for a moment by the grave. One of the boys saw me and came back.

"Sir, I wonder if you would mind doing something?"

"Sure, Henry, what's on your mind?"

"I hope you understand what I'm trying to say, sir. I know this fellow buried here is a Communist and everything, but I wonder if you'd say a prayer for him and for his family?"

"I understand what you mean, Henry. I'll be glad to." I bowed my head, and Henry bowed his. We prayed.

"Chaplain, could I see you a minute," a voice called out.

I opened my eyes and looked around. It was Captain Brakowski. "Be right over. I'm sure sorry to hear about Stenson getting hit, Spence. He was a fine young fellow. But I'm glad that Albright and the sergeant were just brushed."

"I know what you mean, Chaplain. I wanted to ask you what you would think about having a service out here this afternoon. Some of our men are pretty shaken about Stenson getting it. As you know, he wasn't liked too well among the men, but he had only thirteen days left before he was to rotate home. When the 'short-timers' don't make it, everyone starts thinking. His death really got to some of them. A religious service would help things, I think."

"Several of the men asked me about a service today so I had already planned to conduct one right here. Originally, I had scheduled a service for when we would get back to base camp, but I agree with you. I think we need one now."

"Good deal, Chaplain. What time would you like to have it? We'll pass the word around." We agreed upon six P.M., after the men had chow but before it got dark.

A couple of helicopters landed with hot chow. After the men had been served, they drifted off in small groups to eat.

"Protestant service in five minutes," someone yelled. "Over here for Protestant services."

The men started to gather in the specified area. I greeted them as they walked up and pointed out their 'chapel'. Actually, it consisted of two branches tied together to form a cross. The men sat cross-legged on the ground. One soldier passed out the hymn cards. Captain Brakowski and Sergeant Goodman sat in the first row, and Peavy sat just behind them. Albright did not join in, but he lounged against a tree a few yards behind the rest.

The group sang two hymns, but the singing was pretty bad. It is possible that some of the men in the unit had fine voices, but they must have been the ones who didn't make the services today. In the middle of the second hymn, we were so far off key that it took a sustained effort and a large degree of courage to even finish the verse. As we finished, we all broke into laughter. Then I began my sermon. Even though I seldom had the opportunity to prepare sermons in advance, I tried to give attention to the situations at hand. When we stopped for the night, I got around among the men as much as possible. I believed the ministry of "thereness" was vital. But regardless of the difficulty of preparation, I was most serious about my preaching—knowing full well that any sermon I preached might be the last one some of them would hear.

Today, I talked about the potential for good and evil that man had within him. I referred to the war in which we were engaged to illustrate the evil that men can inflict upon each other, and I referred to the various men who had, on the other hand, benefited mankind immeasurably by their lives and contributions. Pointing up the fact that we could choose whether we would be a plus or a minus in society, I added that we, of all people, must realize our limitations, and that much was beyond our personal control. After making a few additional appropriate remarks, I brought the sermon to a close. A number of the men paused to thank me. Soon they had all scattered and were getting ready to bed down for the night.

As I walked away, I heard Albright's voice. "Chaplain, you don't really believe that stuff, do you?"

"What do you mean, Alex?"

"I mean that philosophical premise that all men have some good in them. You don't really believe that, do you, Chaplain?"

I sat down by him as a couple of other men gathered around. They waited for my answer. "Alex, I believe very much that every man has a vast potential for good and evil and that each of us must decide which we will exert. What is your feeling about it?"

"Chaplain, I believe the world is made up of animals, some with four legs and some with two, but they are all animals just the same. You know, it's like they say, you can take a pig, dress him up, send him to school, give him a manicure, and even make him an officer in the army, but the first time he passes by a pigpen, he'll jump right back in. He was born a pig and he'll always be a pig."

"Do you mean to say that you really think everybody is a hypocrite and no one actually holds to a value system or lives by his principles?"

"Exactly. I believe this and I can prove it."

"How do you propose to prove such a thing?"

"I'll challenge you, Chaplain. I've heard your nice illustrations about how much some of your good men have done for society, but frankly, I don't buy it. I haven't met these fellows yet; I've just heard stories about them. But I do know what real men are like. Now, Chaplain, I've listened to your sermons; I challenge you to listen to mine and let's see which will hold water."

"I'm not sure I follow you, Alex. What do you mean by 'your sermon'?"

Albright sprang the trap. "Chaplain, here is my sermon. When we get back into base camp, I challenge you to go into Saigon with me and let me show you what real life is all about. I'll give you a ringside seat to watch the kind of guys you've been calling good. We can wear civilian clothes and no one will know you're a chaplain. How about it? Are you willing to go out on a limb to see if your sermons are true?"

Before I could answer, the men who had gathered around laughed and one of them said, "He's kinda got you on the spot, hasn't he, Chaplain? If you don't go, it's sure gonna make you and your sermons look bad."

I knew that this G.I. couldn't care less about any sermon of mine, and that he really wasn't too interested in what anyone felt about me. He was only taking a good opportunity to let out a little hostility. But on the other hand, some of these men might not be able to see through Albright's argument. Not to accept his challenge would seem to them to be the defeat of my convictions. So I made up my mind.

"Albright, you want to challenge me? Okay, I'll toss the challenge right back to you and your buddies. I'll go with you if you will be in chapel next Sunday to hear my sermon. That will give my answer to what I saw in Saigon with you! Is it a deal?"

Albright was stopped in his tracks for a moment. His challenge may have started out as a bluff, but now he had to go through with it. One of the men standing nearby yelled, "No stalling, now, what do you say, Albright? You and your buddies gonna meet the Chaplain half way or are you gonna back down?"

"All right, Chaplain, it's a deal. You go with me and I'll give you an education you probably missed in the seminary. And then we'll be in the front row the next Sunday in chapel to hear what *you've* got to say."

*Chapter Seven*

## "*You Ain't Lived Till You Tried It Once*"

Long lines of helicopters brought the troops back to base camp. The men were grimy and caked with dust, weary of constant tension and with nerves showing it.

As they sat in the choppers, some of the men had their feet hanging from the side doors, and their faces told a story which words often cannot. Some were talkative and their chatter was made up of bad jokes and trivialities. Others reflected deep-seated uneasiness. Some sat quietly staring into the distance. Their silences were remembrances of horrors which they should never have seen, and which, after having seen, they could never forget. Others were loud and boisterous about their activities of the last several days. This was no more than fear becoming articulate.

In a matter of minutes after the planes left the clearing in the jungle, they flapped their way back to the air base at Bien Hoa. As the choppers touched down, the men jumped out and headed toward the trucks that were waiting to transport them to base camp about two or three miles away. When the trucks were packed full with standing men, they pulled away, one after the other.

Very shortly, everyone was back home again. That is, back at the nearest thing to home they would have until that great day when they would be rotated back to the States. When the men first arrived at this base camp a few days, weeks, or months ago, it seemed like the very end of the world. It was an accurate picture, they thought, of Viet Nam. However, now that they had been on several operations out in the jungle, this base camp had become real "city living." But it had not changed at all. They had.

The area was dotted with tents. Endless dust had colored them a nasty yellow, and where the tents had sagged, the dust accumulated. Heavy rains had taken their toll and the canvas was rotten. New leaks appeared with every downpour. The life of these tents was supposed to be about one year. These were much older, but no new tents were expected.

Two wooden structures served as mess halls. The men scrounged the lumber and negotiated a little "midnight requisitioning" so that everyone could eat in a real building. The ingenuity of the men was unbelievable.

The "theater" had one wooden wall, which served as the screen—no top, sides, or floor. Benches were available for the first arrivals. The rest stood, brought a chair, or sat on the ground. A few metal bleachers in the rear were for officers and NCO's. It took about a month of steady theater attending to adjust to the discomfort of these privileged seats. After that, a man became numb in the spot most in contact with benches.

The unit owned one projector. The projectionist and his equipment were housed in what looked like an outhouse on long legs. The current was brought in from a generator which hummed noisily during every movie.

Rain fell each evening after about fifteen minutes of the movie. The new men could always be distinguished from the old-timers by the way they ran for cover when it rained. The veterans sat through every downpour as though unaware of the drenching they were getting. What difference did it make? They were wet all the time anyway.

Many of the movies were reruns, but, regardless of the age of the film, everyone looked forward to it. The technicolor world on the screen was far better than the one the men saw when the screen grew dark.

In addition to regular feature length motion pictures, various television films were shown. Everyone liked "Gunsmoke." Matt Dillon, Chester, and Doc were favorites. Another regular was "Combat." The men would be in actual combat all week, return to base camp for a rest, and then for relaxation watch "Combat"!

When the trucks were first unloaded at base camp, the men dashed for their tents. The greatest thing in their world at that time was a cold shower. They could hardly wait. Who can describe fully the refreshing experience of just taking a bath when you have been without one for days? The shower was a crude affair—four poles stuck in the ground with a piece of canvas wrapped around three sides. It had a wooden floor and overhead was a big tub that had to be filled manually before each shower.

The water was always cold unless it had been in the tub long enough to be warmed by the sun. What a thrill it was to reach up, turn the knob, and feel that clean water. It was too good to end, but others were always waiting impatiently.

Shaving was another base camp treat—even with cold water. The clean feel and pungent aroma of shaving cream and the scrape of the razor was just one more tie with the "normal" world. And usually this was the first time most of us had combed our hair in several days.

On the first day back in camp the brass sort of eased up on the G.I.'s. Everyone took care of just necessary duties and had the rest of the time for cleaning up and getting his gear into order.

One of the tents was used for the P.X. Long lines formed in front of it, and as men came out of the rear door, they were loaded down with everything imaginable—cases of beer or soft drinks, cosmetics, boxes of cookies and candy bars, gum, toothpaste.

I was sick of lines. Everyone stood in line for something. There was the toilet line, the P.X. line, the sick call line, the barber shop line, the pay line. I decided that when I got back to the "world," every time I passed a line, I would spit and then keep walking.

As the sun rose higher each morning, the heat beat down harder. That is one place where the jungle had it over the base camp. At least out there under the forest canopy, it was a little moist and cool, but at the camp it was hot, dry, and dusty. Whenever an army vehicle went by, the dust whirled up in thick clouds. Everything was covered with a thin layer of this infernal powder. Nostrils were caked with it and hair was colored by it. My throat was always dry, and I was thirsty all of the time. I would have bloated myself with water except that it left a great deal to be desired. There was no running water, so we had to drive down to the water point in trucks and bring it back in tanks. The water was nonpotable, so before we could drink it safely, it had to be treated. Several water cans were brought to each tent. These cans sat out in the sun all day, and, of course, hot water doesn't appeal much to a thirsty man. When the cans were set inside the tent, the water was lukewarm at best—still not very appetizing. Ice was seldom available. One unit found ground glass in the ice they purchased from Bien Hoa. And when we thought we had located a fairly reliable source of ice on the local market, the price started zooming upward. It reached the ridiculous point, so we bought only enough for use in the mess halls to cool our drinks. However, the supply of ice could not meet the demand, so we rarely drank anything that was really cool.

As the sun settled down on our first day back in camp, the Viet Nam darkness was pulled over us like a long woolen blanket. It was good to be back off the operation and within our own confines.

It was time for the evening movie. All the bleachers and benches were filled—men positioned their chairs all across the field and others sat on the ground or stood. The area was filled long before every showing, since this was the only entertainment available, but it was always packed on the first night back in camp. The men needed something to relax their tensions and every feeble joke in the movie would receive an enthusiastic response.

It seemed that there was always one thing wrong with the projector. At first they couldn't start the machine. After a few minutes of waiting, the men would hoot and catcall. Losing his patience, the young soldier who was the projectionist yelled for any one who could do it better to come on up. But sooner or later the projector would come alive and everyone settled down.

As the title of the film flashed across the screen, there were loud comments. The general mood of the audience was disapproval, but not a man moved from his place. It was television film night. Everyone had hoped for a movie spectacular, a side-splitting comedy, or an Alfred Hitchcock mystery on their first night back, but this was from the bottom of the barrel—a black and white, old television rerun. And to cap it all off, it was from the series, "Combat." Loud jeers went up and the crowd broke into laughter. Still, they liked it.

Men have always liked war stories. It must be a throwback to the competitive urge and masculine aggressiveness which is part of a man's nature. But, in spite of their earlier reaction that audience of battle-weary troopers were spellbound. The irony of it was that the events of war and combat portrayed on the screen were like stories in a third grade reader compared to the realities experienced by these young men just hours before. Still they watched and cheered like a group of school boys.

As would be expected, the film broke at a particularly exciting spot. The yelling, hoots, and jeers began again, until an NCO ordered, "Knock it off; he's getting it fixed as quick as he can."

The movie started once more. Some time later a familiar whining sound was heard and the sky was lighted up momentarily by a flare. Everyone sat motionless. A second flare went up on the perimeter. The movie continued. No one moved, but everyone hoped that nothing would develop. Several spurts of rapid fire broke out. Tracers zipped through the night. Then the sky was dark again and there was silence except for the sound of the generator and the voices of the actors in the movie. There was a sigh of relief. Combat is more pleasant when it is confined to the screen.

My tent was situated just across the road from the theater area. Several soldiers gathered there after the film for Bible study. They sat on the floor with their Bibles in their laps. In the group was one of the company commanders—a lieutenant— Sergeant Goodman, Washington, and five other guys. Following the singing of the few hymns, we had a time of prayer in which most of the men participated. A number of prayer requests were suggested. One matter of special consideration had to do with the trip I was to take into Saigon with Albright. They prayed that I would be guided and that regardless of what I might be taken to see, the resultant situation would help Albright find faith in God and in his fellow-men. Following prayers for the families of men killed in action and for the Viet Cong, we usually closed with the Lord's Prayer.

Each man brought his Bible, but in the dimly lighted tent it was difficult to read the small print. The one light bulb received its power from the same noisy generator that had run the movie. This was the nearest thing to a chapel that was available—it may have looked like an old ragged tent, but to the men who met here, it was the House of God.

Across the field was a building which housed a mess area for the NCO's in one end and a bar in the other. Unfortunately, sometimes things got pretty noisy. For example, during the service on this particular night, three men left the bar and walked past my tent, singing at the top of their voices, "We're three little sheep, we have lost our way, baa, baa, baa." When they heard us singing hymns, one of them said, "Say, here's another party, let's join it," and over they staggered, arm in arm.

When they snatched open the front flap, the men inside had begun their prayers. The three bleary-eyed soldiers saw the men sitting on the floor with their heads bowed.

One of them asked, "Say, what's going on here?"

I opened my eyes and looked up.

The half drunk soldier recognized me and exclaimed, "Oh, hello, Chaplain, you having a party too?"

"Well, in a way. We're having a religious service."

"That's good, Chaplain, we all sure need religion. Any way I can help you, sir, just let me know. You're one of the best chaplains I ever had."

The trooper next to him added, "Chaplain, would you pray for me. I've done some bad things in my life!"

"That's right, Chaplain, pray for us. We've had a little to drink tonight, but we're not drunk," pronounced the third soldier, solemnly.

The three men backed out, "Good night, Chaplain. Don't forget us."

Down the line in his tent Captain Brakowski sat at his desk for a long time, not moving. Finally he took the piece of paper which was in front of him, crumpled it into a ball and threw it into the wastebasket. Taking another sheet, he wrote, "Dear Mr. and Mrs. Stenson, it is with extreme sorrow that I express my condolences to you in respect to the death of your son."

He tore up that page and got another. Tonight he wanted to write the parents of the boys in his unit who were killed on the last operation. By this time the Department of the Army would have made its official notification, but he wanted to write them personally. This kind of letter was always extremely difficult, and he had written far more in the past than he wanted to remember. To some commanders the dead trooper was just a serial number and the letter was merely an official duty. But to Captain Spence Brakowski this was far from the case. When one of his men was killed, a part of him died. He was a sincere, kindly man, and his heart was torn every time he wrote a condolence letter. Sighing, he started over again. . . .

Down the road and across the field was the unit motor pool. In the rear of one of the tents was a vehicle maintenance shop. The flaps were tightly closed, but the light from a lamp spilled out into the dark. Several men were clustered on the floor in one corner playing cards, while one man kept watch. Staggering sums of money changed hands at these games. With the regular airborne extra pay, plus the additional combat pay, plus the fact that there were few places to spend money, the men accumulated large amounts of cash. Some saw this as an opportunity to gamble for high stakes. The winners amassed more in a few weeks than they had been able to earn in years. The losers received letters from their wives pleading for help in their financial emergencies and threatening letters from their creditors. Often in the tension of a series of bad hands, a flare-up would develop and that night or the next day someone was sure to show up needing stitches, first aid for a black eye, or bruised knuckles.

A frame building with a tin roof was used as the officers' mess and officers' club. In one corner of the big room was a bar—in another some lounge furniture. The rest of the room was filled with chairs and tables for mess. Three lieutenants talked about football, college, their plans for the future, etc. After a few drinks their conversation became quite animated and slurred.

Lieutenant McNeil sat at one of the tables by himself. He was working on a correspondence course. Some of his fellow officers chided him for not joining them at the bar. Everyone considered him a good officer, but few thought of him as a man with whom they liked to pass time. McNeil seldom looked up but worked steadily on the military manual, jotting down notes from time to time.

Every bunk was required to have mosquito netting over it. The mosquitoes were fierce and malaria was a constant threat. It was not the least bit unusual to crawl under the netting, fall asleep, and then be awakened by an all too familiar buzz. This happened to me that night. When I came to, there were two or three welts on my face already, so perhaps it was the itching that awakened me instead of the buzzing. Finally I fell asleep again, but turned and tossed. There didn't seem to be any breeze at all. The heat was sticky and my sheets felt damp. And then, artillery pieces opened up just behind the tents. The volleys shook my senses, and the percussion seemed to rattle my teeth. "Won't they ever stop?" I asked myself. They didn't, so I fell asleep again.

Sometime later I was awakened again by the shuffling sound of something running across the floor. I listened and heard paper crackling near the wastebasket. Unable to stand it any longer, I reached down under my bed for a flashlight and aimed it toward the sound. On my desk two large eyes picked up the light. It was a large, ferocious rat. By setting traps, these rats can be caught every night, but there are always more that come to take their places. Some men have been attacked in their bunks by these savage rodents. When I banged on the floor, the rat ran away, but he would be back later.

I woke up early the next day. Out in the field we were always ready to move out by dawn, so the habit just stuck with me. Then too, it may have been the anticipation of going to Saigon. At any rate, I lay in my bunk enjoying the early breeze and the quietness.

Every morning trucks took troops into the city for a day of relaxation. During his stay in Viet Nam, each man would have his turn on two or three occasions. The trucks left early and then picked up the men about an hour before dark.

Sergeant Goodman was stacking packages into the back of a smaller truck. He, too, was going to Saigon today and seemed to be taking a great deal of luggage with him. Since he was a first sergeant, he was able to get his own transportation. He had one of his new troopers with him and they were making the trip together.

Captain Brakowski was making preparations to go to the city. He was interested in obtaining a quantity of tin to be used in constructing barracks and a dayroom for his men. Sheet tin was almost impossible to obtain through regular channels, but he decided to act now. He had his hands on a small fund for which no one had official accountability, so he had decided to buy tin with it. He had a Vietnamese friend who worked in Bien Hoa who told him about a close friend of his who lived in Saigon. This friend was a prosperous Vietnamese businessman, and because of their friendship, he would be able to get the tin at a very low price. Plans had been made for a meeting, and the captain was to pick up his friend (called "Jimmy" by Americans since they could not pronounce his real name) and take him to Saigon to meet the businessman.

Captain Brakowski reached over and took his shirt from its hanger and was surprised to see a large hole in the side pocket. Unsnapping the pocket, he looked inside and saw a sack of candy that had been left in the pocket overnight. A telltale hole was in the corner of the bag. During the late hours one of the rats had chewed a hole through the pocket to get to the candy.

Meanwhile, the truck with the men from Alpha company pulled into the parking lot at the Ambassador Hotel, one of the American rest and recreation headquarters. The men jumped out and disappeared into the city. This was the first trip for Washington, Reed, and Mathis, and they were all eyes as they walked along.

The sidewalks were lined with Vietnamese hawking all sorts of trinkets. It was almost like a county fair back home. Some of the little places were run by children, some by the very elderly, and some by whole families.

"Over here, G.I.," one boy called out.

All three of the soldiers looked back. The youth motioned for them to come over to a bench where he had a large box of trinkets.

"You soldiers have much money," the lad said in broken English. "You want buy girl friend a present?"

"We don't have any girl friends," Sammy Reed said.

"You don't have girl friend?" the boy asked, as though the thought was incredible. "You are American Airborne and no have girl friend? Sergeant," he said, speaking to Washington, "you buy this necklace for two thousand piaster?"

"I'm not a sergeant," Washington replied.

"Oh, you must be officer. You wear nice clothes. You rich."

The three men laughed. "How much does this necklace cost?" Leroy Mathis inquired.

"Two thousand piaster."

"How much is a piaster?" Sammy interruped with a puzzled look on his face.

"Captain," the boy began, "I like American Airborne so I give you real good deal. See this necklace. All girls like this very much. Since you my friends, I give it to you for just twenty American dollars cash. Nobody else give you this kind of deal."

Washington scratched his head. "Well, we sure thank you, but that's still a lot of money. We don't have no girls to give them to anyway."

"O.K., O.K., I'll tell you what I'll do. You buy the necklaces and I'll get you girl friends. They'll be much happy when you give them necklaces. See, we real friends."

"No, no, we don't want no girls. We got enough problems already," Leroy laughed.

After talking for several minutes, the three soldiers walked away, each carrying a necklace in his pocket. They were convinced they had gotten a good bargain and felt a twinge of guilt about the boy coming out on the short end. None of them needed the jewelry, but they had bought it for less than half price and could always give it to a sister or girl friend back in the States. What a deal at just ten American dollars! The boy had insisted that they sold at about fifty dollars in the big downtown stores.

They continued to feel good until they saw the same necklace in another store priced at one hundred piasters—about one American dollar, nine dollars less than their "bargain." Each face reflected disgust, but none of them mentioned seeing the cheaper jewelry. They had received their education in "Saigon shopping" in one easy lesson.

Mathis, more sophisticated than the others, had the next idea. "Hey, why don't we get one of those Oriental massages they all talk about? They say you ain't lived till you get one."

Washington answered with an air of worldly wisdom, "Oh, that's just where they rub your back and put all kinds of good smelling oils and lotions on you."

"That's for me, fellows. Are you with me?" Reed interrupted. So off they went to look for a massage. Soon they came to a sign picturing a man getting a massage, with the word "massage" written in English.

The three men walked in and found themselves in a luxurious waiting room. There were several overstuffed chairs and sofas, lamps, thick curtains, and an expensive carpet. At one end there was a business counter with a man and a woman behind it. The woman smiled, "Good morning, would you like a massage?"

"Yes, how much?" Washington asked.

"It will be ten American dollars each."

"What do you think? That's a lot of money," Reed said.

"That's not so bad. Let's go ahead; there won't be any massages back out in the field."

"Well, it's up to you guys. I just want to show you a good time," Washington said, trying to appear very much in command of the situation. Actually, he had never had a massage in his life, and he had no idea what would happen. But he wanted the other two men to think he had really been around.

Mathis plopped a ten dollar bill on the counter. The other two followed. Then they all stood there waiting to be told what to do.

The man behind the counter walked over to a window, motioning for the soldiers to follow. As the men peered through the window, they saw a group of about ten girls dressed in shorts and loose blouses—some more attractive than others.

"What do we do now, Washington?" Reed asked.

Before Washington could answer, the woman spoke up, "Choose the girl you want to massage you."

This was just like looking through the nursery window at a hospital at newborn babies. But these girls were not babies. They were all ages, shapes, and sizes.

"I feel funny, Washington. I bet they do too."

"Naw, this is the way they make their living. That's just the way they do things over here in the Orient."

When the three soldiers had pointed to three different girls, they were called and reported to the counter. Each girl was handed a towel and introduced to the man who had selected her. She took him by the hand and led him upstairs. The hall was lined with doors, each opening into a small room.

As Washington walked into the small room with the girl, his confidence vanished immediately. He had no idea what to expect next, and since his two buddies were no longer present to be impressed, his curiosity and doubt ganged up on him and caused his previous self-assurance to disappear. There was a bathtub, a massage table, a cabinet full of various powders and oils, and a stool.

"Take your clothes off, please," said the girl.

"What?"

"Please take your clothes off," she repeated, taking off his coat and unbuttoning his shirt.

Washington stepped back quickly, embarrassed.

The girl smiled, handed him a towel, put it around his mid-section, and motioned for him to take off his trousers.

"Well, I never thought this could happen," Washington muttered. But soon he was sitting in the tub with the towel wrapped securely around him. From the tub he went to the table, and the Vietnamese girl gave him a dry towel to put around himself.

"Hey, Washington," Mathis called from another room. "This girl is trying to stand on my back. Is she supposed to do that?"

Washington watched his girl as she took off her slippers and climbed up on his table. His mouth dropped open. Standing on his back, she shifted her weight slowly from foot to foot! This was followed by a hard massage. It was very relaxing, and had Washington not been so uneasy as to what might happen next, he would have fallen asleep. But the spell was interrupted by a buzzer—the signal that the hour was up.

The three soldiers arrived downstairs at about the same time. They each had a sheepish smile. With an attempt at sophistication, Washington commented, "I told you there wouldn't be much to it."

# Chapter Eight

## Stay Out of Here, Little Nigger

Sergeant Goodman sped down the road in the army truck. He had asked a new arrival in the company to drive for him. The boy, Freddie, looked as though he was about fifteen. Actually, he had just turned seventeen and his parents had signed for him so that he could join the service. Freddie was homesick, and Sergeant Goodman had noticed it. The boy had been crying one night and, of course, was kidded mercilessly. He ate very little—had a hard time sleeping, and because he was on edge, he made mistakes in the simplest of duties. The thoughtful first sergeant felt this trip would be good for him.

Sergeant Goodman had also asked Albright to go along. At first he had objected, since the sergeant had made it clear that this was not an official duty and that he didn't have to go. Albright, realizing that the trip was optional, said that he would go if the sergeant really needed him, but that he did have a few things to do around the base camp.

Goodman, aided by many years of experience in handling soldiers, knew exactly how to let it be known that he expected a certain action from a man without stating it as a specific order. Albright got the message and said he would be happy to give a hand. He could take care of his other matters when they returned. Sergeant Goodman had applied this gentle pressure because he felt that Albright had a problem that he needed to talk about. Not only had the soldier jumped at every opportunity to challenge the chaplain, but his way of doing it implied more than just hostility to religion or religious views. The sergeant sensed that a war was going on within this young man somewhere. He had noticed that his jabs were becoming more caustic and cutting. The old soldier felt that the young trooper needed a valve through which this steam could escape, and he hoped that during the trip he might himself become that valve.

Also, he didn't like the rumor being spread by the men that Albright was forcing the chaplain to go to Saigon. He knew that the chaplain had accepted the challenge, but it seemed to him that Albright was taking advantage of the chaplain's sincerity. He wasn't sure that Chaplain Grayson was prepared for what Albright would probably show him in Saigon.

"Over here," the sergeant told his driver. "Go through that alley."

The truck barely had room to go down the narrow alley. The young soldier drove cautiously.

"Now, Freddie, we've got to take another right turn at the cabinet shop. You'll have to turn as far as you can, back up until you touch that fence, and then cut back to the right as sharp as you can."

Albright chimed in, "Sounds like you've been here plenty of times before, Sergeant. You don't have a home away from home back here somewhere do you?"

"You know better than that, Albright."

When the vehicle turned down the next narrow road a tiny voice yelled, "It's Sergeant Goody." Instantly they were swamped with ragged little children. They appeared from all directions and climbed up the slowly moving truck.

"O.K., this is fine. Stop right here."

As the sergeant stepped out of the cab, the children climbed all over him. They were smiling and all talking at once.

"Boy, I wouldn't put my hands on them," Freddie told Albright. "Look how dirty they are. They'll probably steal his pants off if he doesn't watch it."

"Help me unload the packages and we'll take 'em inside."

Freddie jumped up into the back and started lifting out packages. The children gathered around—all were poorly dressed and obviously had become accustomed to doing without. Their noses ran and several coughed deeply. They were filthy, and flies crawled over the open sores on their poor bodies. Deep in their eyes you could see heartbreak and sorrow. Their hugs and affection were the reflection of hungry desperation.

But at the same time, they were alive, expressive, and direct. Forced by circumstance to learn the rules of survival, their little eyes never missed a fragment of food on the ground or any discarded item which might have some small value. The poverty into which they had been thrust by the accident of birth never robbed them of their innocent laughter.

"Men, this is the 'Open Door' orphanage," the sergeant said proudly. "When a little child wanders down this alley with no other place to go, the door is always open. There are about fifty-five children here, in quarters which should accommodate only about twenty. It's not much of a place, but it's better than nothing at all."

"Sergeant," Freddie asked, "won't their own parents take care of them?"

"Freddie, many of them have no parents. Either they were killed in the war, or they died or they just couldn't support any more children, so they left them in the street. See that cute little blond over there and that little boy with the dark skin? They, and many like them, were born when some G.I. passed by but wasn't around to help them when they needed him. The mothers were shamed by the birth and left the child to die or to be claimed by anyone."

Laughter interrupted their conversation. Albright was on all fours riding two little boys on his back like a wild bronco. He was bucking and they were laughing. Finally, he lifted them off and sat down to catch his breath. A little girl with black pigtails and big sad eyes walked up to him. Without a word, she sat on his lap, put her arms around his neck, and pressed her face against his chest.

"I brought that little girl here," Sergeant Goodman confided to Freddie. "Her mother and father were killed by a bomb dropped from our planes. I found her sitting alone on what was left of the charred floor. She was so sick from exposure and hunger that the only sound she could make was a whimper. I brought her here and she surprised everybody by living."

"Let's go inside and take a look." It was very plain. Ragged pads were packed in one corner of the room. There was scarcely any ventilation. Children were everywhere—some sat quietly on the floor and some played.

Albright, moved by what he saw, asked, "How do they get food and clothing?"

"Alexander, they just do the best they can. Their government gives them a little now and then, but they really can't depend on it getting to them. And when it does, it's not enough to meet their basic needs."

"Well then, how do they get by?"

"I've been coming up here as often as I could for several months now," Sergeant Goodman answered. "I've been bringing all the food that I could talk the mess sergeant out of and have bought some stuff myself. Some of our men give a few dollars each month, and with everybody's help we've been able to keep the doors open."

"I'll sure give something when I have it, Sergeant," the young soldier volunteered, eager to help out.

"Yeah, me too, Sergeant," Albright added. "Just let me know how much and when."

"That's nice of you guys. I'll sure keep you posted. But I didn't bring you here for a touch. What some of these children need more than anything else is just a little tender loving care. I thought maybe you'd like to play around with some of them for awhile, and then if we have time, do a little repair work here and there." As the sergeant talked, it was easy to see how interested he was in these children and how happy he was helping them. "Sounds great to us," Albright said. "Right, Freddie?"

"You bet, just show us where to start."

The men brought the packages in and unwrapped them. All sorts of old C-rations rolled out on the floor. Cans of milk were stacked in a box. Three well-worn sleeping bags were included as well as several discarded shirts and pants. There were five bags of Vietnamese food that Goodman had purchased. He couldn't resist including a little candy.

An hour or so passed. The sergeant was looking for an opportunity to get Alexander alone. "Say, Albright, what about giving me a hand with this fence over here?"

Albright came over and sat down on the ground by his side. The sergeant handed him a board and asked him to pull the old nails out. Goodman had a facility for getting men to open up to him, and when he listened, it seemed as though he really cared about what a man said. He was easy to talk to.

As they worked together on the fence, the conversation opened up and Albright talked freely for awhile. But then he closed the door abruptly lest he let too much of the real Alexander Albright show. The sergeant steered away from any subject that seemed to upset him.

Albright's mind drifted back to his youth, and he began to fit the pieces together. "From the earliest time that I can remember, there was something about my family that I hated. It bugged me, and even though I didn't understand what it was, I was always aware that there was something that embarrassed me."

"What was it that seemed to get to you?"

"Come to think of it," Alexander continued, "this is the first time I ever really talked about this thing openly. I think maybe I was ashamed of what was happening to us and ashamed that I felt so strongly about it all. Sergeant, sometimes I get sick when I think about how violently I've let myself react against the finest parents who ever lived."

"Hand me another one of those boards, Alex."

Albright passed him a piece of board and continued, "Yeah, that's what's such a damn shame about it all. My parents were so fine, but so stupid."

"What do you mean, stupid?" Goodman asked.

"Sergeant, would you ever believe it? I was a minister's son. Can you beat that, Alexander Albright, the son of a preacher?"

He looked quickly at the sergeant to get his reaction, but Goodman continued with his work and showed no special surprise at all.

"What's so stupid about your father being a minister?" he asked casually.

The soldier seemed relieved at the matter-of-fact response. It was obvious that this topic was loaded with emotional dynamite.

"Sergeant, from the earliest time that I can remember my mother and father were cutting corners to make ends meet and scraping the bottom of the barrel so as to account for every crumb. They both wanted an education so, as my mother said time and again, that they could give something to the world. The trouble is, we did all the giving and none of the receiving. After making it through college, both taught school for awhile, but my gullible father wasn't satisfied. He wanted to be a minister. Everyone told him how much he was needed in God's work and that they were sure he had the 'call.' They all offered their prayers, but that's the only thing they ever gave him."

"What happened then?"

"Hell, what happened was that my mother had to teach full time, teach piano on the side, and take whatever jobs she could find weekends and in the summer. She probably lost several years of her life just trying to get Dad through seminary. But

I'm not criticizing Dad; he poured out his blood, too. He didn't take a full load at school, but worked eight hours a day in addition to his studies. I was born during those days and when Mom had to quit working at the last possible moment to give birth to me, Dad had to work even longer hours just to keep some food in the house.

"Well, he finally graduated. He had really earned that little paper certificate they presented him. But after all their hard work there was nothing to show for it but a certificate framed on the wall. They had sacrificed everything. Mother had worked all day and Dad had studied all day and worked most of the night, just to get that paper."

"I'm not sure I see your point, Alex. You were ashamed of your parents. It seems to me that you would have been proud of them. They had more backbone than most of us would have."

"You haven't heard the full story yet, Sarge," he explained. "I'm not so much ashamed of them as I am of what happened to them. In fact, I'm very proud of them. Well, anyway, Dad was called to his first church. Actually he had two small churches, each in a different town. You know what I remember from these first years?—being cold in the winter because proper heat wasn't provided in our house. Mom and Dad refused to mention it to the church members because, they said, the furnace would have been repaired if the church could have afforded it. I remember looking forward to visiting our parishioners with Dad because their homes were warm.

"Another thing that sticks in my craw is how empty our house was. We just didn't have any furniture when Dad finished school. He and Mom bought some old broken junk that they tried to repair just to get by. Some of the church ladies criticized Mom for not taking proper care of our furniture when they saw how run down it looked. When I walked into her room and saw her crying, I hated those women.

"But I don't mean to paint too bleak a picture of my family. We had a great time together. We would play games, tell stories, and take walks through the country. After a time things got a little better financially. Mom budgeted the money carefully. Instead of buying toys, she bought us books—instead of going to movies, we attended recitals and concerts. Every night we spent two hours reading. During those hours an appreciation grew within me for knowledge and inquiry. I became hungry to learn and was taught that the most profound question in the world is "Why?"

"A little brother was born into our family during those years. Dad named him Timothy because he had a feeling the boy would follow him into the ministry and be a 'Timothy' to him like Timothy in the Bible was to Paul. Dad felt so close to Tim that I can see how I might have been jealous, but I never was.

"After a time, we were called to another church in a large city. It was a much larger church, but Mom and Dad discussed the move for several weeks before making a decision. The church was in a very bad part of town. Negroes were jammed together in a rough section that was rundown and full of hate and crime. It was not that my parents felt too good to live and work in an area like that, but they were concerned about us. They realized that we would have to grow up in a jungle of back alleys, crowded streets, foul air, and that our neighbors would be liquor heads, dope pushers, and pimps. But at the same time my father felt divinely ordered to take up this particular ministry. He said that he was called to serve and that the greatest need would constitute his greatest opportunity. We were all convinced that we should move to this new place for service and that God would take care of us.

"We were right about the challenge of it all. Dad moved into his new work quickly. Large numbers came to hear him preach, and very soon he became known as a sincere, devoted, and hard-working man of God.

"But it was rough. Young hoods smashed the stained glass windows. Perverts were caught in our sanctuary late at night, and the church office was broken into repeatedly.

"My father discovered that dope addicts were active among some of our young people. After much effort, he traced the source of supply to a prominent citizen of the community. He accumulated sufficient evidence before making the charge. Dad was threatened, hit by a brick, and warned of the results that would follow if he presented his case. My mother received obscene telephone calls, and my brother and I were roughed up. Still, he gave his evidence to the authorities, and the trial date was set. Just before the trial was held a teen-age girl in our congregation, who was involved in the dope ring, pressed charges against Dad for rape. This blew the top off our church community. It was obvious that this was simply an attempt to bring suspicion upon Dad. His trial dragged along for months and finally he was declared innocent. But then there was a movement within our church to ask the pastor to leave because of the bad publicity. This hurt him deeply, and though he was completely innocent and everyone knew it, he gave a great deal of thought to leaving because, as he said, he didn't want the Kingdom to suffer. As much as Mom would have loved to leave, she encouraged him to stay. She knew that his heart was still there.

"Little Tim and I came through it, but not without some scars. It was during these days that I found out I was different. I had never before really noticed that my face was black and that a Negro is third-rate.

"One day at the trial, Tim kept pulling Mom's sleeve, asking to go to the bathroom. Finally she asked me to take him. We went down the hall to a door with 'men' written on it and walked in. A slovenly man said, 'What are you doing in here, boy?' I said I was taking my little brother to the restroom. 'This room ain't for nigger boys. Git out of here. If you know who your daddy is, tell him to take you back in the alley. But stay out of here, little nigger, unless you want to get in trouble.'

"As we walked out, Tim asked me what a 'nigger' was. I didn't know how to explain it. Of course, I knew, but it just hadn't made any difference before. For the first time in my life the two most important colors became black and white. And we were on the black side.

"The dope trial which followed hit on this distinction again and again. My family had been poor before, but we had never been looked down on. We had never been considered second class. But now I was old enough to understand why.

"Maybe you can understand the shock we experienced when a white man called us 'little bastards,' and our anger and frustration when the realization dawned on us that he had a right to say it because he was white, and that we had to take it because we were not.

"I rebelled against it all. Here was something that made a lie out of almost anything that I had been taught. As I grew older, I began to consider the values my parents had lived by as ridiculous.

"Tim reacted differently. I know he was aware of it all because of the questions he asked, but he never seemed to be embittered. There was no doubt, he had the 'call.' He was cut out to be Dad's Timothy all right. But I was up to here with it all. I was sick of 'understanding the situation,' of praying for our enemy and all that jazz.

"Even though Tim and I were different, I admired him. We all felt that he was the one marked to do great things. He had the 'call,' the gift, the temperament, and that strange restlessness within that would drive him on to make his mark. I guess he inherited that spark that refused to be confined to a Negro's world where you know your place and stay there.

"Our parents insisted that each member of the family learn to play some instrument. Tim chose the organ. He was not musically inclined, but due to his discipline and persistence, he learned to play.

"I chose the trumpet and took to it like a duck to water. My father didn't like it when I jazzed up the old hymns, so in his presence I stuck to the simple orthodox productions. It wasn't long before I was in demand at some of the school parties. I improved my style, organized a combo, and in a short time was making more money on the weekends than Dad was making full time at the church. My reputation reached the nightspots and I had it made.

"Remembering what a rough time Mom and Dad had experienced and knowing how little they had available to send Tim to college, I promised myself that I would see to it that he went first class. So I started a special fund for Tim. I knew that he had what it would take intellectually, and that if he just had a chance, he would go far. My contribution to society would be to provide him with that chance.

"I had been out of high school for six years and was living in my own small apartment. Tim was excited about the prospect of getting to a large university, and Dad was happy in his work. He was very concerned about the integration problem and felt that he should encourage Negroes to be conciliatory rather than aggressive. I differed with him in that I thought Negroes should forget prudence and claim their constitutional rights on the spot. But there was no use arguing.

"Tim was notified to report to the draft board. He explained that he had been accepted by the university, that he was in the top five percent of his class, and that he planned to study for the ministry. Any one of these reasons was good enough to make him exempt from the draft. He was given his physical and a temporary classification but was reminded that the classification could change and to stay in close contact with their office.

"It was at this time that something happened that almost shattered our world. Dad told me about a demonstration by a Negro organization that was planned for the next day. He said that several of the leaders of the group were friends of his and had confidence in him, but he was worried because he felt that they were hotheaded and impulsive. Dad believed in their ultimate cause but was afraid that they might create trouble. He planned to encourage the leaders to be moderate—nothing must happen to spoil the progress already made between Negroes and whites.

"The next time we saw Dad he was in the hospital. As he had approached the Negro group, some foul-mouthed white man threw a brick. It hit my father on the temple, and he fell to the ground unconscious. He never regained consciousness and died three days later.

"Before we could recover from this tragedy, we were struck again. Tim was called to the draft board and reclassified. He was to be called to active duty immediately. I questioned the gentleman in charge and he simply said the war in Viet Nam was requiring more men. When I reminded him of Tim's reasons for being exempted, he said the final word had been given and that he didn't make the decisions. He said we could ask for another hearing, but that it would have to be after Tim was in the service since his induction date was near.

"When Tim arrived at basic training, he was told that a hearing could not be arranged at that time and that the matter should have been taken care of before he was actually inducted. They suggested that he recheck his status after he had completed basic training.

"Immediately after the training he was given a brief furlough and put on orders for Viet Nam. We just couldn't believe it. In the few days that he had, we tried unsuccessfully to force a hearing. We were told that we couldn't expect special treatment and that every American should be proud to serve his country.

When I cited all the others who were not called, the draft board casually answered that everyone could name someone who hadn't had to go yet. I volunteered to take my brother's place, but they laughed and said they couldn't run the army like that.

"Within thirty days after Tim arrived in Viet Nam we were informed of his death. We should be proud of him, they said, for he died in defense of his country.

"I'm not sure Mom will ever get over it. She lost too much too quickly. But I don't want to get over it. I want to keep on remembering how my brother, who some white slob called a 'little bastard,' and who was constantly being reminded that he should be grateful that his colored presence was tolerated in this white man's world, was murdered in this white man's war.

"Sergeant, for weeks I didn't want to see anybody; I didn't want anyone to say anything to me. I wanted to comfort my mother, and I tried the best I could. But deep down I knew I was being a hypocrite. How can you comfort someone unless you know of something that can give hope—unless there is some meaning somewhere that can cause some of the pieces to fit together? The only thing that had meaning to me was hate.

"Some well-meaning friend of the family tried to comfort me by speaking of God. I stood up and shouted 'damn God.' Where is that fellow they call God? I don't think He's really up there anywhere. I think the expression 'God' is just a name for the ideals of people like my Dad and Mom and little brother who want to give something worthwhile to society. And if this is true, then this 'God' business is a farce because the world isn't interested in the things that good people offer.

"Well, to make a long story short, I had nothing but hate in me. I signed up in the army and volunteered for Viet Nam. I wanted to take Tim's place and finish the job he'd started. I wanted to kill somebody. I wanted to even up a score. It may not make sense, but that's why I'm here. Don't think I'm patriotic. This is a white man's world and a white man's war. I'm here to take care of my own war. And do you know something, Sergeant? No matter how far we hike through these jungles and no matter how much dying we see, I still haven't seen God hanging around anywhere to help."

# Chapter Nine

# *A Real Cool Character*

Captain Brakowski and his enlisted driver picked up Jimmy, the Vietnamese, and drove to Saigon. Spence wanted to spend the fund he had as quickly as possible, and the tin seemed just the right answer. He was happy that he had Jimmy along, for he didn't know much about Saigon. Having a contact like this would not only get a great deal more tin for the money but it would also save time. He wasn't in the mood to haggle all day from shop to shop, as was the usual procedure.

Jimmy was a real cool character. He was still in his twenties but had already laid aside a good-sized bank account. In addition to being a sharp dresser, he spoke English very well and knew all the right people. This helped him in his work as an interpreter for the army. Jimmy worked hard, but his chief asset was his ability to "wheel and deal."

It wasn't that Jimmy was dishonest, but he had a knack at making the most of any situation. For example, when he heard through one of the officers that a garbage pickup program was needed, he sprang into action immediately. Jimmy worked behind the scenes and employed a Vietnamese to act as manager, and through his position with the army, he soon had a contract for the job.

He had a quick eye for business and was wise enough to realize that the time to make money was while the American forces were still in the country. A financial boom had occurred overnight in Viet Nam, prices had soared to unbelievable heights, and the way to make money was transparently clear to the Vietnamese—just find out what the Americans want and provide it.

Jimmy majored in this philosophy, and he decided to by-pass a university education, which was a matter of great status in Viet Nam. In his mind, the flood of money would not last forever. The time to make his fortune was now. Everything else could wait.

Jimmy borrowed enough money to rent three small buildings,

each in a different location, two in the city and one near a
military installation fifteen miles away. He hired fifteen girls to
serve as hostesses and opened his bars. The overhead expense
was negligible. The basic commodity for sale was the smiles
and giggles of the girls.

When a soldier walked into the bar, all the available hostesses
flashed a glance of invitation. He would choose one and sit with
her in a small booth, and she would order drinks for them. It
was supposed to be wine, but the girl's glass would contain
colored water, humorously referred to as "Saigon tea." The
charge was one dollar for her drink and one dollar and fifty
cents for his. The girl received a percentage of the profit she
earned. She was a delightful companion and ready to talk as
long as he kept the drinks coming, but the second they stopped,
she asked to be excused.

Soldiers packed the bars and seemed to be happy to leave
their money. After all, they had plenty, so why not have a good
time with it? Jimmy liked this arrangement. If they were going
to throw their money anyway, he would certainly be glad to
take it.

Within two months he paid back all the money he had borrowed. Business was good, and with his bars and few other
investments, Jimmy would be independently wealthy within a
year.

Captain Brakowski directed his driver to park the jeep at the
Rest and Recreation Hotel. This was an authorized location
where military police were on guard. If a jeep was left unat-
tended anywhere else, a bomb might be stuck under the fender,
and anything left in it would be stolen once the driver was out
of sight.

"Jimmy, I want to do a little shopping before we go over to
meet your friends. If you'd like to go along, you're welcome."

"Sir, be O. K. if I call my friend first and then I go shopping
with you?"

"Sure," responded the captain.

Jimmy motioned toward a shop and suggested that he make
his call from there. Brakowski stood by his side listening to a
long-drawn-out conversation in Vietnamese. It was beyond his
comprehension how anyone could understand this jabbering and
grunting.

When Jimmy finally hung up the captain asked, "What in the world were you talking about that took so long?"

"My friend, Mr. Woo, is very happy that you will honor him by being his guest. He would like for you to stay overnight."

"That's very good of him, Jimmy, but I've got to get back to camp. Did he mention anything about the tin?"

"Oh, don't worry, sir, he already take care of that. He will have tin at house when we arrive. No sweat, sir. Jimmy handle it for you. What you want to buy? Maybe I save you much money."

"Well, Jimmy, I thought I would look at some of these Oriental watches and then get a chair and a small carpet for my room. Where would be a good place to go?"

"Sir, don't buy any jewelry in Viet Nam. The watches look number one on the outside but they are number ten on the inside. They steal your money. Be much better to buy watch at P.X."

"Thank you, Jimmy," Brakowski grinned as he spoke. He was amazed at the paradox of the Oriental mind. Jimmy was as shrewd as they come, but with an American friend, he was completely open and honest. Captain Brakowski found this combination very attractive.

"Sir, never try to save money in the Orient. The Vietnamese know of American's desire to get what you call 'a bargain.' Everything is made to look like a bargain. We are very good at making the cheap article attractive. If you want something you call Jimmy. I get it for you. When you walk in any store in Saigon, they will up the price at least three times because you are American. They know Americans have plenty of money."

"Jimmy, it seems to me that if your people realized we're keeping the Communists from taking over the country, they'd treat us fairly. I wonder if the Vietnamese want us here or not. What do you think?"

Jimmy didn't hesitate at all, "Captain, most of my people want the Americans here. They know what the Viet Cong are trying to do. Of course, many of our people not educated; they only know what they are told. In every village in Viet Nam the Communists are talking to these people every day. They are teaching doctrine, enlisting members from each family, and organizing for the future. They point out to our peasants that

Americans are bad people. But just as important, is what is happening in our country because American forces here. Your standard of living much higher than ours. Your salary probably higher than that of our top general. Your enlisted men make two or three times more than our officers. So when Americans come with all their money, you can see what happens. You can pay more so we charge more. Shops that once catered to Vietnamese now sell exclusively to Americans. Everything is aimed toward the American market. Things that a few months ago every Vietnamese family could buy are now too high.

"And another part of the problem, sir, is what this does to the family. In Viet Nam the family is very important. Families determine who children will marry. The father is boss. All members of family work, and everything is part of family.

"But, sir, notice what happening today. In the past, the father was the breadwinner. He earns from eight to twelve dollars a week. This met the needs of his family. Today this not meet basic needs. Everything cost more. So, daughter beg her parents to let her work at a bar as hostess. At first they won't even listen. A few years ago such a thing unheard of. If girl do such a thing, she would be cast out by her family. Even though she can now name several of her friends who work in bar and who are bringing home big money, still the parents will not dignify the matter even by discussing it. Finally the girl gets job without telling parents. She makes more first week than her honored and hardworking father make in six weeks. Her job never mentioned again, but the parents know, and each week money is left on the father's table. The father has lost face in his own family. He is humiliated. Even his ten-year-old son makes more money. Son sells cokes to the troups passing by on the road.

"So, Captain, bitterness grows among my people. Not so much that they hate Americans, they just hate what has happened. Their way of life is gone, and only things they can see is American soldier who swaggers along sidewalk with a roll of money in his hand."

Captain Brakowski scratched his head. He was totally unprepared for what he had heard. "Jimmy, I never thought of it that way. I see the problem."

"It's much big problem, sir. Even our young men becoming very angry. Harder now for them to find a good wife. The

American with all his money gets all the beautiful girls. Only the fat ones or the ugly ones are left. A few months ago if a Vietnamese girl was seen with an American, she was looked down upon. She was considered a prostitute, and no one would be friends with her. Today it is changing. Some of the girls marry the soldiers and become wealthy in comparison with their friends. Even the lowest private has P.X. privileges and his wife can have lots of food and clothes. It is too much to expect girls from poor homes to refuse all of this. As more and more of our girls marry soldiers, the standard is forced to change.

"Our young men cannot compete any more for the girls. They hate the Americans for this. When they see all the beautiful Vietnamese girls working in bars and nightclubs just for Americans, they get angry. Even if the Vietnamese youths were allowed in these places, they couldn't afford to pay the prices.

"The Communists show our men pictures of Americans with Vietnamese girls. The pictures show girls sitting on G.I.'s laps, hugging and kissing."

"Well, Jimmy, I'm sorry about all of this. Maybe someday it'll be straightened out. I can see how you would be bitter toward us and wish that we would leave."

"I don't wish Americans would leave. We have problems here all right, 'sorry-bout-that,' but I'm a businessman, not a politician —it's their job to solve problem. My job is to make money. If they work as hard as I do, pretty soon we have no problems."

Captain Brakowski could not help but laugh at Jimmy's sincerity and crazy philosophy. At least he was honest.

"Sir, where do you want to eat? You have place in mind?" Jimmy asked.

"No, I thought I might take you to the officers' club, but it makes no difference to me. What about you? Do you have any preference?"

"Any place you like, sir, but I do know a number one Vietnamese cafe. Have you eaten any Vietnamese food yet?"

"No, I haven't."

"I take you to number one place. Food very good. I'm sure you will like. This way."

Before long they were sitting in a small Vietnamese restaurant. It was off the beaten track, quiet and unhurried. There were no Americans. It had a comfortable and friendly feel about it.

When they were given menus, the captain was perplexed. Everything was written in Vietnamese.

"Captain," Jimmy suggested, "I will order for you. I know some very good food which you will like very much."

In a few moments the food was on the table. The captain looked at it suspiciously. On his plate was rice, something that looked like spaghetti, a raw fish, and little round objects that looked like eyeballs.

Jimmy made the sign of the cross and began to eat with great relish. His manner of eating was messy, but his enjoyment was obvious.

Captain Brakowski, stalling for time before tasting his food, asked, "Jimmy, I noticed you made the sign of the cross. I thought everyone over here was Buddhist."

"Oh, I'm Protestant, Catholic, and Buddhist. I figure if one is okay, three must be three times as good."

Captain Brakowski had no answer for this. Holding his breath, he began to eat.

"You like Vietnamese food, sir, it good as I said it would be?" Jimmy asked.

"Yes, Jimmy, it's really great," Brakowski lied, as he gagged to keep from throwing up. How could you tell a man as nice as Jimmy that you don't like his food or that you would give a week's salary for an old-fashioned hamburger? In the name of peace and friendship between nations and for the sake of Vietnamese-American relations, Captain Brakowski finished the food on his plate. Jimmy was determined to pay for the meal, insisting proudly that the captain was his guest.

When they got back to the jeep, Jimmy directed the driver to the home of his friend who lived outside the city. After riding several blocks, he asked the driver to stop. Saying he would be back shortly, he hopped out and disappeared into a store. A few minutes later he came out carrying a chair and a rolled-up carpet.

"You like these, sir?" he asked the captain.

"They're just what I wanted. How much are they?"

"No sweat, sir," he answered matter-of-factly. "They are my gift to you."

Captain Brakowski tried to hand him some money, but Jimmy pushed his hand away. "Please, sir, put money away, they my gift to you. You are Jimmy's friend."

As they drove along the city streets, people were everywhere. Taxi cabs, military vehicles, motor scooters, and bicycles moved past hurriedly. The area through which they were passing would make the slums in the States look good. The small mud huts with tin walls and thatched roofs were no better than shanties. Children filled all the empty spaces.

A few blocks further on they entered an area with elegant homes, obviously housing only those who were wealthy. Jimmy told the driver to turn down a small road to the right. The lane dead-ended at a big gate.

They honked, a yardman opened the gate, and they drove into a large estate. There was a courtyard with a number of outbuildings, with the main house off to the right.

In front of the spacious porch was an Oriental garden, serene in all its exquisite beauty. Trees and shrubs were placed artistically. In the center of the garden there was a tiny island with an arched bridge leading to it. And everywhere there were flowers, flowers, flowers, thousands of them.

As the jeep came to a stop, a handsome Vietnamese stepped from the front porch. Jimmy jumped out and said, "Mr. Woo, I would like you to meet my friend, Captain Brakowski. Captain Brakowski, this is an honored friend of my family, Mr. Woo."

Mr. Woo extended his hand and smiled. Since he spoke very little English, Jimmy interpreted, but from time to time, Mr. Woo did attempt brief statements in English.

He led the group inside where they chatted for a long time with Jimmy interpreting. After a time he told Captain Brakowski that their host had apologized for the hot weather and suggested they go out to the patio.

The captain insisted that they must leave since it was getting late and he did not want to travel after dark. When Jimmy relayed this to Mr. Woo, he stood up suddenly and said "No, no, please be my guest." He attempted to continue in English but obviously was unable to do so. "I am very sorry," he apologized, "my English very poor."

He continued in his own language. Jimmy explained that their host would be honored if they would spend the night in his home. He suggested that they could talk for awhile longer this evening, have an early breakfast, and leave at whatever time they wished.

After initial objections, Brakowski agreed to stay. It would be a treat to spend one night away from camp. Also, it would be good to sleep in a real house for a change.

When he decided to stay, Mr. Woo was delighted. The party moved out to the patio where cushioned chairs had been placed for them. It was dark and a cool breeze blew from across the river. Brakowski had almost forgotten how wonderful civilization could be. Sitting back, he lit his pipe and relaxed.

The host showed his guest a family scrapbook and pointed proudly to pictures of his parents, his children, the buildings he had constructed, and the cattle he was raising. The pictures made Brakowski homesick.

Mr. Woo asked Brakowski how the people in America felt about the war. Would the American people support the president? How did he like Viet Nam and the Vietnamese people? Did they seem very different from his own people? He talked on and on, confiding that one of his investments was in timber and that he owned many acres about thirty miles outside of Saigon. He said that the Viet Cong controlled the area and that he had to pay them to permit his men to cut lumber.

It was an interesting fact that he and most of his close friends came originally from Hanoi in North Viet Nam. From the way Mr. Woo talked about his early years there it was clear that it meant a great deal to him. He described the trees that lined the streets in Hanoi and said that actually the northern part of Viet Nam was the most beautiful of all. He longed for the day when he could return to the home of his youth.

He hated the Viet Cong. It was because of them that his family had to flee from their home in Hanoi, leaving behind a fortune which his father had earned from a lifetime of hard work. Shortly after they arrived in Saigon his father died, largely due to heartbreak.

Mr. Woo mentioned a brother who was still in North Viet Nam and was serving as an officer in the Viet Cong army. He said that he was ashamed because of his brother's identification with the enemy. Before his father died, he had contacted the brother through friends who were still in Hanoi and begged him to give up his affiliation with the Communist government and to join them in South Viet Nam. He replied that he would join them in Saigon in the future, but it would be when the People's

Government had taken over. They never heard from him again.

After a long pause, the captain cleared his throat diffidently and mentioned tin. Mr. Woo looked pained. Apparently it was not proper to discuss business in a man's home, but Mr. Woo smiled and nodded and managed to convey the impression that all was well.

He spoke to Jimmy in Vietnamese.

"Sir, Mr. Woo would like for your permission to receive his wife and children and to introduce them to you. He said that they would be greatly honored."

"I was wondering where they were," the captain said. "I heard some giggling and noticed some little fellows peeking around the corner every time the door opened. I was a little surprised they hadn't come in already. Back in America they would have stormed the room before now. Tell Mr. Woo it would be *my* honor to meet his family."

"Captain, things much different here. If wife or children show their face in presence of guest before being invited by the father, it is considered very rude and the father loses face. In Viet Nam the man is the boss, sir. No sweat, they do what we say."

Jimmy spoke again in Vietnamese. Mr. Woo smiled at the captain, bowed his head slightly, and stood up. He walked to the door and opened it. His wife entered first, bowed, and stood with her eyes cast down. From behind her came an apparently endless line of children beginning with a boy of about eighteen and working on down to a child who could barely walk. There were eight children. They all bowed at once.

Spence was impressed. He said, "Jimmy, tell Mr. Woo I like his family. He is fortunate to have such a lovely wife and fine children."

When Jimmy relayed this message to his host, he bowed twice in obvious pleasure and pride.

"Thank you, Captain," he replied, "they are number one."

He then walked along the line of children looking at each one proudly. In his broken English he said, "See Captain, I very good Catholic, have much children."

This startling announcement signaled the end of the evening, for very shortly Brakowski, his jeep driver, and Jimmy were shown to their rooms.

All three slept soundly.

# Chapter Ten

## Sin City

Captain Brakowski dropped Jimmy at his home and arrived at the base camp on schedule.

As soon as the company commander reached his tent, the CQ notified him that the battalion commander had called a special meeting for all officers in thirty minutes. It was rumored that another operation was in the making.

The officers gathered at the officers' club where the colonel gave his briefings. The operations officer hustled in with several maps rolled up under his arm. The intelligence officer and the supply officer were deep in conversation. A guard paced around and around the tin building. It was obvious that something important was about to break.

Within minutes after the briefing opened the secret was out. The general had got word of a Viet Cong battalion operating in the Iron Triangle. He wanted to check it out; the second battalion was selected to go. They would leave in two hours and in less than thirty minutes after takeoff time the choppers would set them down right in the questionable area.

In about an hour the troopers boarded the large cattle trucks to be carried to the "snake pit," the soldiers' name for the area at the air base where the helicopters were boarded for take-off. A few minutes later they lined up by the long rows of helicopters with forty-five minutes left before take-off time. Some of the men stretched out on the paved strip and slept. Others gathered in small groups and played cards. Some joked and laughed. Every man wondered how this next one would be. No one ever really thought that any mission would be his last, but everyone considered the possibility.

"Saddle up," someone yelled.

The men jumped to their feet and strapped on their gear. The choppers hummed and shook with the vibration of the powerful engines. Eight men climbed on each plane and waited.

The waiting was agonizing—it gave each soldier time to think.

Most knew the story all too well from here on out. In a matter of moments the point of contact would be made, and from there on it was anybody's guess. The men made cracks, sounded off, and engaged in horseplay up to this point, but the moment of truth was always fearful.

The tremendous propellers revved up and the 'copters rose one by one. The doors on both sides of each chopper were left open. Four men sat on a row of seats and four others sat on the floor.

The countryside below was a vast green panorama. Villages dotted the landscape—women were busy near tiny houses and men were working in the fields. It seemed out of character to be weighed down with ammunition and weapons. But to those who had been on this journey before, the peaceful scene only reminded them of the paradox of war—of the harsh fact that the enemy was always near.

In the distance smoke rose from a spot in the jungle. This indicated an artillery unit zeroing in on a suspected enemy target or an air strike based on an intelligence report. Everywhere below were circular indentations. They looked small from the air, but they were large craters caused by the American five-hundred-pound bombs.

One cannot but feel sorry for the peasants who, under the name "Viet Cong," are herded from their villages in North Viet Nam into the jungles of South Viet Nam. Their tour of duty in the VC army was not just one year—it was an endless string of days and weeks and months and years. They were on the move constantly, creeping and crawling through the steaming jungle. If they were detected by observation aircraft, U. S. artillery and air strikes poured explosives on them. There was no end except death. In the past they could pull back to their rest areas, but now there was no place safe from American harassment. And yet the long lines continued to edge into South Viet Nam. One wondered if they never asked what happened to the men who went before them. When they were told of their mounting "victories" against the "Yankee aggressors," did they ever doubt? Apparently not. They just kept on dying and being replaced.

The choppers touched down one by one and the men jumped out and scrambled for cover. Just as soon as they were emptied, the helicopters took off, and in a few moments it was quiet again

and several hundred men crouched in the grass waiting to kill or
to be killed. Nothing happened. Either the Viet Cong were not
here, or they chose to play a waiting game. Step by step the men
moved toward where the enemy was supposed to be.

Regardless of how many times this happened, it was still a
tense and disagreeable business. Whether a patrol ran into heavy
enemy fire or just walked along quietly, it was the same. Every
man knew that at any second he could be framed in the sights
of sniper's rifle.

They walked all day. Finally, it was time to bed down. It
would be good to get in the sack, though, of course there was
little real sleep in the field. The fact that guards were set up
was comforting, but the idea of sleeping under the very noses
of the enemy—the idea that they might have us under observation
at this very moment—made sleep pretty much out of the question.

As I crawled into my hammock, I felt a slight sting on my leg.
I got out and soon found the trouble. A leech was embedded in
my leg. When I was unable to pull it off with my fingers, a buddy
handed me his cigarette, and when I touched the hot end to the
leech, it turned loose.

My pants and boots were soaked from jungle travel, and sleeping in wet clothes was never the easiest thing in the world for
me. But from experience I knew that it was taking too much of a
chance to sleep with my clothes off.

Just as I was about to fall asleep a swarm of mosquitoes
attacked me. By the time my tired nerves responded to their
hungry assault, I was covered with bites. The night was hot and
humid, but my only protection was to wrap up in a thin blanket.
After a time, somehow or other, I fell asleep.

As the sun rose the next day, preparations were made to
continue the search. The four companies of the battalion entered
the wooded area in front in long parallel lines. The men traveled
until about noon and took a break for chow. It looked like an
easy one this time. The word was that they would go back into
base camp tomorrow morning if no contact was made by then.
Everyone had hoped for an easy go of it, but Lieutenant McNeil
was chomping at the bit. He insisted that we were here to win
a war, and we couldn't do it unless we found the enemy and hit
them hard. Perhaps he was right, but he was a career soldier—
he wasn't born; he was issued from some supply depot.

Bravo Company moved out first after the break with their first platoon leading the way. As they started, the lieutenant called to the soldier who was acting as point man, cautioning him about walking into an ambush. "Slater, we know they're out there somewhere waiting for us, and we have to play the game their way. You've got a reputation for being careless. For God's sake, keep your eyes open."

"Sir, you don't need to worry about me. I won't let my buddies down; you can be sure of that."

Slater moved forward as point man. This was his first time to be given that responsibility, and he was eager to prove himself.

Headquarters Company was taking its break. The RTO for the colonel informed him that the first platoon of Bravo Company had moved out, and that it was approximately fifty meters off to the right. The colonel nodded assent.

Just then a terrible explosion shook the forest. Everyone in Headquarters Company hit the ground. Leaves were dislodged from the trees and floated downward. There was a momentary lull and then automatic weapons broke loose.

"Those are Viet Cong weapons, sir, I can tell by the sound."

"Get on the phone," the colonel directed. "Find out what's happening."

The radioman talked briefly into his instrument, and reported, "Sir, all I can get is that the first platoon of Bravo Company made contact. That's all they know. Wait a minute, sir. He says they're hit real bad and are pinned down. A Claymore mine got them and now snipers are on both sides."

As suddenly as the heavy firing had started, it stopped. All was silent.

"Sir," the RTO spoke again, "They're calling for medics. They need all they can get. Their medic is dead."

"Medic," someone yelled. "Get over to the Bravo area."

The colonel was on his feet, snapping orders. "Get on the phone and get some troops in to help. Sergeant, send some of our men in there on the double. Move out."

"But, sir, they're calling for medics."

"Hell, medics are no good with those snipers shooting them as fast as they come in. Get some fire power to them first and then get the medics in."

Soldiers scrambled down the trail to the site of the explosion. The scene was appalling. Wounded men lay on the ground where they had been hit.

One soldier stood dumbly and stared at the still face of his best friend, who had received a direct hit in the chest. A medic was working over another soldier whose skull had been crushed by a shell. The man had never known what hit him.

"Medic, move on to someone else," an officer instructed, realizing the man was dead.

"Sir, they just keep lying there and I can't make them get up. Why won't they say something, sir?"

"Sergeant, give the medic a hand. Take him over to the back area and have him sit down for a while. Have another medic look at him."

Some distance away another medic knelt beside a soldier who was lying on his back. It was Slater. His side was torn open, and his ribs protruded through the torn flesh. Slater's face was pale and his pulse weak.

"Medic, please get the lieutenant for me. I've got to see him."

It was obvious that the youngster was dying. The medic had done all he could, and it was useless to do anything more. It would just be a matter of minutes.

"What do you need, Slater? I'll take care of it for you."

"No, I—I must see the lieutenant; he's got to know something. It's important."

"O. K.," the medic assured him, "if it's that important, we'll get him. Just hold on. Don't strain; just relax, boy."

The dying boy held on for thirty minutes. It was obvious that only his grit and determination kept him alive. His body was virtually dead. Only his determination was still living.

The lieutenant was trying to check on the patrol. He had sent up a smoke bomb so that the incoming choppers could land and pick up the dead and wounded. Twice, word had reached him that Slater wanted to see him. He didn't know what the boy's condition was, so he waited until he could handle some of the other problems first. When the message reached him the third time, he realized the seriousness of Slater's condition and hurried to the young trooper's side.

"Slater, how is it?" he asked as he eyed the smashed body.

"Sir, I'm real bad. My side hurts bad and I am so weak. I know

I am not going to make it, but I wanted to hold on until you came."

"Can I do anything for you?" the lieutenant asked. "Just anything, Slater, and I'll do it if I can."

"Sir, I just wanted to tell you that I am sorry. I didn't see anybody. I didn't let the men down. Tell them, sir, that I didn't let them down. The Viet Cong were hiding in tunnels. Be sure the men know it, sir. It means a lot to me."

"Sure, Slater, I'll see that they all know. Don't worry."

Slater smiled and whispered, "Thank you, sir, airborne." He closed his eyes and died.

The area was a beehive of activity. Small trees were bent down and sand was swept across the field from the wind made by the landing helicopters. Nine dead bodies, covered by ponchos, were laid side by side on the ground. Sand and loose dust gathered on the ponchos, two of which had been blown off by the 'copters. The lifeless faces of the two exposed bodies had accumulated dust. A soldier stooped down and closed the eyes, and then replaced the loose ponchos.

"All right, be sure we have all their gear, weapons, and ammunition, and let's get it all on the chopper with them. Some of you men come over here and help get the KIA's on board."

I reached down and placed my arms under the back of the first corpse, the sergeant gripped the feet and we carried the body to the helicopter. Five others were also placed on board.

"I'll go with them, Sergeant, and be sure they are taken care of."

I climbed over the bodies and sat on the floor. Glancing down, I noticed that blood was dripping from one of the ponchos onto my pants. I couldn't help but wonder if one of those boys had been in my congregation Sunday. Only a few moments ago each of them had been alive and full of plans for the future, but now they were cargo.

As the chopper lifted off, one of the boy's arms fell over into my lap. The wind rushing through the open door blew the poncho off his face. I stared at the expressionless face. In just a short time some wife or mother would receive that dreaded letter. Somehow, in respect to them, I wanted to be here as their representative—to just sit by as a friend since there was no one else who even knew. Even though the war was all over for them now, it just didn't seem right that they make this trip back alone.

Within a few minutes the chopper touched down and the bodies were taken off. I uttered a prayer as they were taken away. The plane continued on to the base camp area to refuel. I decided to go on with it and stop by the hospital to visit the wounded who had just been taken in.

The hospital was a series of tents within the Brigade area. It wasn't fancy, but there was everything needed for emergencies. The complex may have had the appearance of a number of ragged and dust-laden canvas buildings, but inside was the latest medical equipment and a team of young doctors, highly trained and accustomed to handling the most complex cases.

It was dark and the daily rain pattered down. Puddles of water gathered, turning the powdery dust into mud. As I entered the surgeon's tent, I noticed unusual activity.

"Say, Bill, what's up?"

"Some unit was just hit hard and medical choppers are on their way back bringing the casualties."

A beam from the searchlight on a medical evacuation chopper pierced the darkness as it made its approach. A team of medics ran out to unload the casualties. The moment the chopper touched down, they reached for the litters and lifted the men out.

Just as soon as one chopper lifted off again, another one made its approach. This went on for hours. The efficiency was superb. Even as casualties were being carried from the choppers to the tents, the doctors worked over them. No time was wasted.

I was sickened by what I saw and went outside to get some fresh air. Limping toward me was one of my men. It had already become apparent that this was not only my unit, but it was the same Bravo Company that only a few hours earlier had its first platoon hit by the mine and snipers.

"What happened out there? Aren't these men Bravo Company?"

"Yes, sir, Chaplain," the soldier answered. "It's almost all of our second platoon. Sir, it was terrible. They don't have them all in yet."

"How did they get hit?"

"Sir, one of our own jet planes dropped its load on us. We had radio communication with the plane, gave them the location of the VC trench up in front of us, and he came in right on our nose. He made three runs on us before we could stop him, and sir, it was hell. There was no place we could go, nowhere to run. From what it looked like to me almost the whole platoon was right in the middle of it. I saw the lieutenant and the sergeant go down. I didn't see anybody who wasn't hit somewhere. It would have been bad any time, but we were being hit hard by the Viet Cong, too."

"Is the chaplain out there anywhere?" someone yelled from the door of the surgeons' tent.

"Yes, over here."

"Chaplain, a man is asking for you. He's real bad. You'd better run, sir."

I dashed toward the tent and was directed to one of the stretchers over on the side. The soldier had already received all that medical help could provide, but it was too late. He had bled too much. The dirt on his young face stood out in contrast to the paleness of his skin. His hair was tousled and mud was caked across his sideburns. He looked so innocent and so out of place on the stretcher.

With lips quivering, he asked, "Someone please tell the chaplain to hurry. Is he here yet? Chaplain?"

"I'm here, son." I placed my hand on his. He was trembling as he gripped my hand and drew me closer.

"Chaplain," he began faintly, "what does it feel like to die? Does it hurt? What does it feel like, Chaplain?"

I was at a loss for words. Yet the young soldier was waiting intently for an answer.

"Son, I don't know, but I don't think it hurts. I think it would be much like falling asleep."

"Sir, if I can keep my eyes from closing can I keep from dying? I'll get better if I just hold on for awhile, won't I, Chaplain?"

"Just do the best you can. These are fine doctors, and they'll give you the very best they have."

A faint smile formed on the boy's face. His grip tightened on my arm. Pulling me a little closer he asked earnestly, "Sir, do you know it before you die? It doesn't slip up on you, does it? I'd want to know so I could get set. And, Chaplain, do you think if I die, I'll go to heaven? I've not been a Christian always. I've done some bum things in my life. Is there a chance?"

"Son, God knows your heart. If you love Him, He knows it. And He forgives the past."

The soldier seemed relieved. For a moment he had a surge of strength and lifted his head slightly. "Chaplain Grayson, if I don't make it, and get to Heaven first, I'll tell them what a fine job you're doing in our unit." His grip relaxed. His head sank back on the pillow, and his eyes stared upward. He had been wrong. A man can die with his eyes open.

The next morning the battalion came back in. It had been a bad operation. They achieved their mission, to some degree, by locating a little nest of Viet Cong, but that was about it. If a larger force was out there, it simply moved back or went down into the tunnels when the G.I.'s arrived. Of course, as quickly as they left the VC probably returned to where they were originally. So the significance of the day's activity was thirteen men killed and forty-four wounded. It would be summed up in the papers back home as "light contact with the enemy and few U.S. casualties."

                *         *         *         *         *         *

"Well, Chaplain, what about it?" Albright asked. "You still willing to accept my challenge? If so, I've got an overnight pass into Saigon."

I had very little desire for any bright lights tonight. Somehow it didn't seem right. Vivid scenes continued to cross my mind that refused to fade—scenes of suffering and death. But life must go on.

"Alex, do you really think this will prove anything?"

"Oh, if you want to back out, sir, it's all right with me. All the other guys will understand. I think they'll realize that all this—I mean no disrespect, sir—all this bull about every man having some good in him is just a professional statement that you ministers are expected to make. They won't press you personally on the matter. They all think you're a good guy."

My back stiffened. Albright was forcing the matter, and he knew it. Even his smooth approach and respectful manner didn't conceal the razor sharpness of his attack. This was a fight to the finish and Albright was choosing his weapons.

"Alex, you know my belief that the divine image of God is impressed to some degree on every man is not a professional requirement but my own personal conviction. If you are challenging my personal faith by this proposed tour, then I have no alternative. Yes, I'll go, but I assure you, nothing you can show me will destroy this belief. It's not worth your effort."

"Now, Chaplain, I certainly don't want to impose upon you or cast any reflection on your sincerity, but it's just that I thought one night out in this real world would settle the question far better than any argument of mine. Our thinking was that we'd like to hear you preach on the subject after you had been in the real classroom of life for one evening. Our whole gang will be in church Sunday if you dare to test what we say."

I was experienced enough to know that I was being "had"— that Albright was masterfully laying me up for the kill. I had heard about some of the bull sessions and how Albright had engineered heavy betting over the matter. The odds were that I would not see it through, or that even if I did, I wouldn't bring it up in my sermon the following Sunday.

I knew that I'd let this get out of hand, but what could I do? Maybe somehow God would untangle the mess. At any rate I'd have to see it through the best I could.

"Albright, I'll be ready to go this afternoon when you are. See you then."

The day passed quickly.

"Sir, it's time to go."

I was somewhat surprised to see Private Gus Jenkins and Albright standing outside my tent, dressed in civilian clothes.

I was even more surprised to learn that Jenkins was going along. He was a big fellow who ran around with the men who considered themselves tough—the hard core "swingers."

"Chaplain, the guys thought that since so much interest had been stimulated by this little affair that perhaps it would be well for one of them to go along as an observer. Gus volunteered. You don't mind, do you, sir?" Albright asked.

"Do you mean the betting is so high now that your buddies feel they need a man on the scene of the action?"

Both looked sheepish. They had no idea I knew about the betting.

"What's that, Chaplain?"

"Oh, nothing. It will be nice having Gus along."

Actually Gus was there to check on me. He was to report back to the gang concerning my reactions, the expressions on my face, and the comments I might make. There would be a lot to laugh about tomorrow, and his job was to note it all down in a little book he carried.

We arrived in Saigon in time for the evening meal and then made reservations at one of the R and R (Rest and Recreation) hotels for the night. It was just dusk, and we stood on the sidewalk in front of the hotel making plans for the evening.

Albright began, "Well, Chaplain, everyone has to be off the streets in Saigon by midnight, so we'd better head out if we want to make the rounds. D'you want to see the two-legged animal kingdom from the gutter perspective first or from the plush high-class angle?"

"Alex, you're in charge."

"O. K., sir, follow me."

"Airborne," Gus responded, emphasizing his support by the way he voiced the familiar paratrooper phrase.

Albright hailed a cab and we crowded into the rear seat. He handed the driver a piece of paper. The driver nodded his head and handed the paper back.

"The first stop on our tour will be an apartment rented by a company whose base camp is next to ours in Bien Hoa, sir," Albright explained. "It has sleeping and cooking facilities and is always open to those who have fed the 'kitty'."

The taxi pulled up to the curb and we got out. It was a nice looking area. Obviously, only the most well-to-do could possibly afford a home in this neighborhood.

We walked past a stone wall to a gate, pushed a button, and the gate man walked over. Albright showed him his identification card and he swung it open. As we walked into the yard, we saw two military jeeps parked there. From all appearances this could have been the home of a wealthy Vietnamese businessman but such was far from the case. We walked up the steps, across the porch, and entered without knocking.

"Come in, please," a pleasant voice greeted us. "How are you?"

Three very attractive Vietnamese girls approached us, smiling as they extended their hands in greeting. Two of the girls had black hair, and the third, in an apparent attempt to look "American," was a bottle blonde. All three wore American style dresses and were heavily made up.

"Hey, what swell dresses!"

The girls giggled, "Thank you very much. They came from the P.X. They would be much expensive downtown. We haven't seen you here before, have we?"

"No, this is our first time here. We're friends of Sergeant Hall in Bien Hoa. He told us to drop by." Albright explained.

"Oh, Sergeant Hall, he is number one. Please have a seat. May we please serve you a drink? What you have? We have whiskey, wine, beer, or would you like for us to surprise you?"

Albright and Gus ordered.

"And what would be your desire?" the blonde asked me as she sat down close to me on the couch. I moved away.

"My name is Toy. What may I call you?"

"Grayson, you may call me Grayson."

There was a stark silence. I had that awkward feeling you have when you're very self-conscious—the quietness dares you to break it and yet threatens you with humiliation if you don't.

Although I felt on the spot and out of place, I managed to say, "I don't think I have ever heard the name 'Toy' before. What does it mean in English?"

The girl answered, "The name is not Vietnamese. It is English word. Some of the soldiers who come here gave me the name. I thought it very pretty so I just make it my name. Everyone call me 'Toy' now. You like?"

"Oh, yes, it's very nice."

"We very glad to see you," the third girl interrupted. "We think none of the other soldiers be able to come this weekend. They go out to field yesterday and be gone for week. Can you stay here for few days? If you can, it will be number one."

"No, we just dropped by to show our friend the house. We've got to go in a few minutes," Albright answered.

"Where you stay tonight?" one of them asked.

"We have a place to stay in Saigon," I answered quickly.

"Oh, I see, you have girls already. But why don't you come here. We very nice. All the soldiers like us."

I got up and walked toward the door. Albright and Gus followed.

The girl added quickly, "If you not like us, there are other girls here, all number one. Please come back."

We walked out of the door.

"Good-by, Grayson," Toy called to me.

As we walked out of the yard and down the sidewalk, Albright explained, "Sir, I just wanted to give you an idea of the creative imagination of our young American soldiers. You see, what they've done is this: A group of about thirty-five or forty men came up with the idea of forming a 'Playboy' club. Each one pays about twenty-five dollars per month, and with that, plus men adding to the 'kitty,' they're able to rent a real nice place. When they can get to the city, the house is waiting for them. Ten girls are employed as 'hostesses.' They are given free room and board and are allowed to work during the day at some other place if they want to. But at night, they have to be on duty if and when any one of the members comes in. So, for just a few dollars a man can have all the wine, women, and song he wants. Some guys pay more in one day in Saigon—and for the same thing —than each of these men pay in a month."

Gus said, "Chaplain, I bet you didn't study about this in school, did you?"

Before I could answer, Albright continued, "If you'd come back here at about two o'clock in the morning, I'd like to see how deep down you'd have to go before you'd find anything worthwhile in these men. Take my word for it, Chaplain, they make the dogs in the alley look good. At least the dogs don't know any better, but these jokers have perfect attendance pins from Sunday school."

Gus had a silly grin on his face as though he and Albright had proved a point. But he wasn't quite sure what the point was.

We hopped another cab, drove some distance, and got out. People were everywhere. It looked like a carnival. A little girl about nine years old came by selling flowers.

"Fifty piaster?" she asked as she followed us. "Flowers very beautiful. You buy maybe?"

We weren't interested, but the child stuck with us. "Twenty-five piaster?" she asked, and looked up hopefully with big brown eyes.

"No flowers," Gus growled, pushing her away.

She frowned and said, "Number ten, you number ten thousand." Turning to me, she handed me a string of flowers and said, "You take free. They very nice."

Not quite knowing what to do, I kept them. Reaching into my pocket I found fifty piaster and handed the money to her.

"No take money," she insisted. "I gave you flowers free."

Finally, I pushed the money in her pocket. The little girl said, "You number one, number one, thank you" and skipped away down the street. We walked on until Albright stopped and opened a door. Immediately we were engulfed in music. Apparently we were in some kind of a club. A waiter led us to a table in the rear. Looking around I could see that even though it was early, the room was already filled with couples.

"We're not ready to order; we'll call you when we are," Albright told him. Drawing up close to me, he continued, "Chaplain, see that group over there in the corner? That's what I came to show you."

There was a group of older men and each one had a beautiful Vietnamese girl. The girls were exquisitely dressed; it was quite apparent that nothing was too good for them. While we watched the party got louder and louder.

Albright continued, "One of my buddies is stationed in Saigon and is a colonel's driver. He told me about some things that may interest you. All those men of distinction over there are big brass. My buddy told me that when his new colonel arrived last month and took over the job of his predecessor, he inherited the first colonel's quarters, office, and girl friend. He said the girl went with the package deal. The present colonel will be the fourth officer she has lived with. The big shots call it their 'home away from home.' With their big salary they can really live it up over here. I thought you'd like to see at first hand our 'Saigon Warriors.'"

The waiter came to the table again and waited impatiently.

"Let's move on," Albright suggested, as he pushed his chair back.

"Say, why don't we get a coke while we're here? I think the waiter expects it."

"Sir, they charge five dollars per coke. If you don't mind, I think I'll wait. I just don't seem to be that thirsty. Come on, let's go, Chaplain, and I'll show you how some of your congregation lives between Sundays."

We walked several blocks through the darkness and then came to a street lined with bars. Soldiers swaggered and staggered up and down in front of the dives. Now and then one would walk out of a bar with a girl, half leaning on her, and stumble to a taxi. In one arm he would have an open bottle and the other would be around the girl. Once in the cab they would disappear into the night.

Several girls were standing just inside the door of one of the bars. As we walked by, the girls smiled and motioned to us. "Let's step in a second and get a coke," Albright suggested. "I'm getting pretty dry."

I was surprised at how small the room was and how many men and girls were inside. The rom was long and narrow—on one side was a bar and small booths lined the other. The hostesses were dressed in the least the law allowed and could speak English fairly well. Some sat near the front of the bar and smiled enticingly when men walked in. Others sat alone, waiting for an interested customer. All were available to any man as long as he kept spending money.

"Come in, gentlemen," came a melodious greeting from a young girl at the door. She wore a tight black dress. It was cut low and had a slit down the side, Chinese style. Her hair was styled in high fashion, and her nails were pink, matching the color of her beautifully curved lips.

We stepped in and returned her smile. Motioning for two other girls to join us, she said pleasantly, "Please sit down and be comfortable. It's very nice to have you in our bar."

As Albright and Gus slid into a booth, two girls sat down with them. I was directed to the next booth, and before I realized what was happening, I found myself alone with the girl in black. Gus was enjoying the whole affair. He had a smirk on his face as he took out a little notebook and jotted something down. Gus had been taking notes all evening. He didn't want to forget anything that would make for a good laugh back at camp.

"Would you like something to drink, please?" the girl asked.

"Yes, I'd like a coke. You get a coke, too."

"Oh, coke is number ten, but wine is number one. I will order us wine."

She was a professional and knew the art of running up a bill quickly. But I was a professional too. It was bad enough to be sitting here in a bar with some Vietnamese girl, but I was not about to buy her wine.

"Oh, no. I don't drink wine, and I don't buy it for others. Let's have a coke; they are number one."

Although I smiled, the experienced young lady sized me up correctly and decided the "pressure" approach would not work with me. She said, "All right, I get you coke and I get myself 'Saigon tea,' O. K.?"

I agreed, and my coke and her "tea" were brought to the table. She had a great deal of charm, and only occasionally did the professional bar girl's mannerisms show through. Designed to throw me off guard, she uncorked a string of questions and comments: "How long you been stationed in Viet Nam? . . . Do you like my country? . . . I think America much better than Viet Nam. . . . Are you married? . . . Do you miss your wife? . . . Are you lonely? . . . You are very handsome—number one gentleman . . . You are not like many of the soldiers who come here. . . Why don't we go upstairs where there is nice quiet room and make love together?

The last question jarred me. I had begun to pick up the trend of her conversation, but I didn't expect her straight fast ball so quickly. I really couldn't think of a ready answer at the moment. Gus was right, none of the courses at the seminary had covered this subject. And then too, I didn't know why I felt so guilty sitting here, but I couldn't help but wonder what my wife would say if she could see me now. Finally I answered her question. "No, I really wouldn't want to do that."

Before I could finish, her smile vanished and was replaced by an expression of disappointment, and she asked in a puzzled tone, "Why, am I not pretty to you? Everyone say I am number one. All the soldiers like me very much."

"It's not that at all. It's just that I am a Christian."

"Oh, that no problem at all. I go get you a Christian girl. Please wait. I be right back."

At this I got up and told the other men that it was about time to go. We paid our bills and left. I never could figure out why her "tea" and my coke added up to two dollars and ninety cents, but I was willing to let them have it.

Gus started to motion for a cab when Albright told him we would get another means of transportation. Parked along the street were vehicles that looked like bicycles. On the front of the bike was a seat with two large wheels on each side. For a very cheap fare, cyclists would wheel you anywhere in the city. Albright spoke several words to one of them, who in turn motioned for two others to come over. Each of us got on a bike and off we went.

We seemed to travel in circles, down one street, off on a side road, through an alley, and back on the main street again. Finally, Albright's bike stopped and ours stopped alongside. It was plain to see—as they say in Viet Nam—this place was "number ten." The street was full of trash, and the buildings were ancient. As we walked down a narrow alley, sickening odors nauseated us. Then we climbed up three flights on a filthy stairway to a hall with numbered doors on both sides.

"We're looking for number sixteen," Albright said.

"There it is," Gus pointed out.

We rapped, and in a few seconds the door opened. It was so dark inside that it took several minutes for our eyes to adjust. The room was small, poorly ventilated, and several girls were sitting on the floor. Their hair was unkempt, and they were only partly clothed. When we walked in, the girls beckoned eagerly. An unshaven man approached, pointed toward the girls, and grunted, "Number one."

Albright said something to him, but he apparently didn't understand. The soldier then rolled up his sleeve and pressed one finger into his arm several times. This sign language sufficed and the man indicated a door at the rear. We opened it and walked through.

Several soldiers were stretched out on the floor. Some had their shirts off—others wore only shorts. One man was over in the corner with a chubby woman, both in a drunken stupor. Another had vomited. Several needles were scattered around. The story was clear. They were all high on dope.

As we left the silly grin was not on Gus' face. He didn't take out his little notebook this time, and Albright didn't make his usual quip.

We walked silently down the stairs, through the alley, and back to the street. As we turned at the entrance of the alley to go down the sidewalk, I paused a moment to look back.

With a sneer on his face, he asked, "Well, Chaplain, what do you think about that?"

Gus waited eagerly for my reaction. The expression on his face turned to one of uncertainty and bewilderment as he was riveted in his tracks by the piercing stare I gave him.

Without a word being spoken, the scoffer was broken and humbled. As Gus stood there staring, I uttered my first and only words, and they tore through the soldier's conscience with the thud of an arrow that had sped through the air and crashed home to its target.

"Father, forgive them for they know not what they do."

They were spoken softly and directed, not just to Jenkins, but to the buildings and the alley and the streets—but to everybody. When Jenkins first heard the words, he wasn't sure that he understood them, but as they sank into his soul, they seemed to stir up some distant memory.

Albright looked at his watch and said, "Well, it's only eleven, but I think we had better get back in. Cabs are hard to find around midnight."

# Chapter Eleven

# Americans Don't Eat People

By noon the next day our trip into "Sin City" was the talk of the camp. Some of the gung-ho officers were surprised that I would permit myself to be taken advantage of by two enlisted men. Others were shocked that I went, but everyone was eager to discover whether I would follow through and preach about my reactions.

The next morning was Sunday, and thirty minutes before it was time for the religious service to begin, the area was crowded. This was especially surprising since word had just come down that the men would leave on another sortie early the next morning. There were always a million and one things that had to be done just before an operation, and unless a soldier asked to be released from duty in order to go to church, it was unlikely an officer would think of it. Ordinarily, men were sheepish about asking to go to religious service since they felt this marked them as sissies. But apparently nearly everyone had asked. Even some of the hard-nosed sergeants who hadn't been to chapel for years showed up. Every available seat was taken.

The sun was blazing down, and since the Command had been good enough to make time available on a busy day, I felt obligated to make it brief. And then, too, I realized why the crowd had gathered. They wanted to hear my response to our trip.

"From the size of the congregation this morning it is apparent that you are aware of my recent tour of 'Sin City.' I am sure your presence here also indicates your knowledge of why I made the tour. Some thought that if I saw all the dives and dens, all the lust and drunkenness, that I would be driven to change my conviction that there is a little good in every man—a little of God even in the worst of us. A number of men challenged me to make the trip and agreed to attend this service to hear my reaction. I would like to respond by making three statements.

"First, I am happy to see that the men who promised to be here are present. This indicates basic honesty, which implies a degree of good in the very men who disagreed with my belief. A few of you may have come out of curiosity, but I suspect that the majority of you came with a secret hope that you would lose your bets. I suspect that you would rather lose the money you bet on the outcome of this venture if in so doing you could find that there is some good in each person. If this has done no more than to cause us to look a little more intensely for the good and to hope that perhaps it is there somewhere, it has been worthwhile. I suggest that each one of you ask yourself the question, 'Would I like to discover that there is a little good in every man?' If your answer is 'yes,' then you have proved my point. Is it not good in us that prompts us to hope to find some good in others?

"Second, some of you were quite correct. I was shocked by what I saw, shocked and saddened—sickened but not surprised. You see, a man who believes in the existence of good is not surprised to note the existence of evil. The good exists, side by side, with the bad. The thing I learned is not that evil exists; I've always known that. I learned how repulsive and appalling the bad really is when it goes unchecked, and how far down a man can fall when he lets go completely. Some of you are wondering if what I saw shook my faith. No, it strengthened it.

"Finally, I want to comment on one thing of which I am absolutely certain. I don't know the answer to all the things I saw. I don't know whether our young men will be mature enough in time to avoid the temptations so attractively set before them. But I do know one thing. The statement of this truth is my text for today and it is the only sermon I have. It is found in Psalm 139, 'If I make my bed in Hell, behold, Thou art there.' Men, all of you know there are numerous hells on every side. Know that if you fall into one, you'll find God there also, still caring and waiting to bring you out.

"Let us pray. . . ."

A few men stayed to talk, but in a very few minutes the crowd vanished. It was anticlimactic. There had been a vast amount of interest in my visit to Saigon and the service which followed. It had been the topic of everyone's conversation, and now it ended with a soft benediction. I felt deflated, somehow.

My enlisted assistant had been rotated back to the United States, and I had asked the first sergeant to be on the lookout for a man to take his place. Since it is always rather difficult to find someone who is just right for the job, I hadn't settled on anyone and was getting concerned because time was running out. In the late afternoon, Sergeant Goodman surprised me by saying he thought he had a man, but had some reservations as to my reaction to him. You can imagine my surprise when it turned out to be Gus Jenkins.

"There must be some mistake, Sergeant Goodman, I'm sure the Gus Jenkins I know wouldn't be interested."

"I knew how you'd feel, Chaplain," the sergeant said, "but Jenkins asked me for the job and I believe he's sincere. He's outside now if you'd like to see him."

I was too surprised to say anything, but motioned to send him in. The sergeant called to him, and left.

When Jenkins entered the room, he was embarrassed and nervous. "Sir, I never have been much on using words. But, Chaplain, I want you to know that every time I've looked in the mirror since getting back from Saigon I've seen a rat staring back at me. What I mean to say is, Chaplain, that I am ashamed of what I am. The few sermons I ever heard in my life went over my head, but Chaplain, I understand what you said Sunday. It made me sick of what I am and made me want to become something I'm not. Sir, I won't feel bad if you don't want me to work for you and I probably don't have much to offer that you can use, but I will promise you one thing: You can count on me to work as hard for you and God as I did for the devil in the past."

I had found a new assistant.

Early the next morning the unit boarded choppers and began another search and destroy operation. We walked for three days. At first the only contact with the enemy was light sniper fire. But at about eleven o'clock on the fourth day, the bottom fell out. As we approached a relatively clear area in the jungle, heavy automatic fire opened up from two positions on the left flank, and a mass of Viet Cong soldiers charged from the front and from the right flank. This was a totally new experience. In the past it had always been a cat and mouse game, never a head on charge.

It happened so unexpectedly that no one had an opportunity to decide what to do. The VC kept coming in suicidal waves, screaming and yelling, blowing horns, beating drums, waving knives, and firing weapons.

One of the newly arrived privates fell to his knee, clicked his weapon on automatic, aimed coolly and fired at the Viet Cong. The man next to him did the same, and down the line it went, until no more Viet Cong were left. The ground was littered with their dead. Surprisingly, we had no KIA's.

For some unknown reason the Viet Cong had determined to hit hard. Ordinarily their method was to chop here and there, claw and wound, then pull back into the darkness of the jungle. But today they had planned to knock out the unit one way or the other. They needed a victory and chose this date on the calendar and this place on the map.

After the charge was stopped, the VC had a small unit just waiting to withdraw and goad our troops into following. We fell for it and found ourselves hemmed in between two heavily armed bunkers. In addition, several snipers were hidden in the trees. We were pinned down. The word to withdraw was given and no one asked twice what was said. We stayed on all fours, crawled backward out of the heat of it and edged out of danger. As we moved out, we radioed for the jets to hit the location where the VC seemed to be dug in. By the time everyone had formed up to the rear, it was almost dark. As we got set for the night, our artillery began to lay a steady barrage into the forward area. The ground shook from the impact of the shells.

"Man, I'd hate to be in their place," one of the troopers said, feeling just a little sympathetic for the Viet Cong, who would have shells rained on them most of the night.

"Say, have you heard the news?" another trooper asked.

"Naw, I don't guess so, what news?"

"About Sergeant Stagg being missing. No one has seen him since our withdrawal this afternoon. Everybody just thought he was somewhere else, until tonight when they all started to compare notes and couldn't find him anywhere. Sergeant Franklin said that he thought he was dead. He saw him fall near the bunker where the automatic weapon was and ran over to help him, but he got hit. He tried to get to him again, but since Stagg was right in front of the nest of 'gooks' and never moved, he finally gave up. They're planning to go looking for him in the morning."

"I don't know what use it will be. Even if by some miracle the sergeant wasn't killed today, it's a cinch nothing could live through all that bombing tonight."

The first thing the next morning a patrol was sent out to try to locate Stagg's body. Sergeant Franklin went along to direct the group to the spot where he saw him last.

"You know," one of the patrol members said, "Sergeant Stagg was a pretty hard guy at times, but he was a good NCO."

"You can say that again. He sure knew his job. He was hard as nails, but that's what's wrong with the army today—we don't have enough tough men."

The little patrol walked along gloomily. The jungle was silent except for an occasional bird call.

No one thought the sergeant would be alive. Franklin's story, plus what they all knew too well about the VC made his death almost a sure thing. Before long they neared the bunker and proceeded with caution.

Franklin found him, and he wasn't dead. Almost, but not quite. Against all regulations they clustered around where he lay, wounded in the shoulder and bloody, but grinning up at them cheerfully. The medic gave him first aid and they carried him to camp in triumph. Sergeant Stagg had made it back.

As soon as I heard the good news, I hurried over to where he lay on a cot.

"Do you want to hear about it?" he said.

"If you're strong enough."

"You bet I am. Well, I got it good—first thing—when they ambushed us. In the shoulder and in the helmet."

"In the helmet?"

"Yeah, knocked me out but didn't hurt me. When I came to, they were all around me. So I just laid there on my back hoping for the best. For about thirty minutes there wasn't a sound. Then I heard some jabbery talk and snipers started climbing down from the trees. Two Viet Cong crawled out of the bunker just in front. Every second I expected to get it. I knew that they always stripped the wounded and dead of every usable item and often mutilated the bodies, so I decided to lie still until just before one of them reached for me and then snatch the grenade from my belt and pull the pin. At least I would take some of them with me. But they hit the ground running. No one took time to check me out or grab my weapons. I guess they knew the artillery and jets would be on them any second. Anyway, they took off. And then those damn jet planes started dropping their loads. I wanted to crawl for cover but I was scared some-body might be watching. After the planes left, the artillery shells started coming in. How they missed me I don't know. But, honest to God, Chaplain, the closest I came to dying was when our patrol found me. I was about half conscious from the blood I lost and from lack of sleep, and when I heard a noise I figured the VC were after me. I pretty near heaved a grenade at them. But I didn't. I recognized it was English I was hearing. Sir, they talk about a cat having nine lives, I know a G.I. who does, too."

The next mission was to locate and search several villages. Most of these would be friendly, but we expected to find one or two Viet Cong villages. The men were ordered not to fire unless first fired upon and not to damage any part of the villages. The orders were to inspect the villages for any Viet Cong who might be holing up there and to carry out the army's civic action pro-gram by helping the nationals in any way possible.

A platoon was sent out to locate the exact position of the villages and make the initial contact. The first village was very close so they were back in just a little while. Four men were chosen to go into the village. The rest would wait until the detail returned. If they were needed, three rifle shots would be fired in rapid succession.

The four men left and were soon in sight of the village. Specialist-four Wright, who spoke Vietnamese, suggested that he and the sergeant go into one of the village stores and that the other three keep watch. They would order a coke and sit around and listen. It was agreed they speak in English so the people would never suspect that Wright understood what they were saying in Vietnamese.

When they went in, everyone smiled and nodded politely. "A coke, please," the sergeant requested and made a motion as though he had a bottle in his hand and was drinking. One old man bowed, showing several gold teeth, and filled two glasses with ice. He poured the coke and handed it to the two soldiers.

As they sat and sipped their drinks, a crowd of Vietnamese gathered. The soldiers talked naturally among themselves but listened and kept their eyes open. The natives stared and chattered away in their own language. From time to time they would break out in laughter.

The sergeant asked, "Wright, can you tell what they're saying?"

"Well, one of the old men pointed to your boots and said he never had seen feet that big in all of his years. The little boy sitting on the box said that it would take very big feet to carry your big belly."

"Come on, don't hand me that."

"I told you the truth, Sergeant," the young soldier answered. "Listen, they're talking again. One man suggested they charge us a dollar each for our cokes because we had plenty of money."

"I ought to smash him one."

"Don't forget why we came, Sarge," the interpreter cautioned.

The conversation continued among the Vietnamese for several minutes. "I think I've heard enough, Sarge, let's go," Wright said. "I'll take care of the cokes."

Wright tossed some money on the counter—about thirty cents per coke which was the going price in Viet Nam. The owner jabbered away in broken English, insisting that the cokes were one dollar each.

Wright answered in Vietnamese, "I don't understand. You see, we're Viet Cong officers in American uniforms, and we came to see if you were our friends. Now, we'll have to tell our commander that you are the friends of the Americans. You may be in much trouble."

There wasn't a sound. Everyone was afraid to say a word.

After Wright explained what he had said, the sergeant suggested, "Tell them that I have been much insulted about their remarks concerning my big belly. Perhaps I can forgive them if the storekeeper will give me some of those bananas."

As quickly as the message was relayed, the owner jumped forward, handing the whole stalk to the sergeant. He stammered, "Please take bananas. Your belly number one; we like it very much. Mine very small and is number ten."

It took a lot of explaining, but finally everything was straightened out. The soldiers left, eating bananas, and the store hummed again with Vietnamese conversation. The first shock was gone and a story was forming that would be retold and exaggerated for years to come.

Many G.I.'s felt contempt for the Vietnamese and thought they were ungrateful. But the situation was really very complex. For instance, they lived in constant fear. About six months before a three-man Viet Cong team of experts had dropped in on the little village visited by Wright and the sergeant. They always came in prior to the arrival of the regular Viet Cong unit. One of the unit was an expert in propaganda. He gave them the works on the glories of the communists, how they tried to help the common people, and how they were in South Viet Nam to help the peasants fight against the Yankee invaders who would enslave them. He painted a horrible picture of the Americans. The second expert was the organization man. He made the village into a smoothly operating and effective communist cell. Informers were trained and a communist leadership organization was set up. The third expert was the terrorist. If one of the village leaders resisted the new organization, he would be found the next morning with his throat cut.

To rebel was to die. Very soon it was made clear that either the village was to become communist or it would be wiped out. These people were simple farmers trying to eke out a living. Certainly they were glad to see the U. S. army, but they knew all too well that its troops would be in their village only a short time and when they left, the Viet Cong would still be in the hills around them. Those who cooperated with the Americans would not be forgotten.

In another village which was predominantly Catholic the communist takeover had been accomplished. One of the teachers in the school who was a strong Christian refused to teach the material which the communists directed him to use. He was taken out one night by a Viet Cong squad and buried alive. The next morning a new teacher was presented to the students. This teacher was a thorough-going communist and did everything he could to rid the students of their religious teaching. In one particular class he pointed out the foolishness of prayer among Christians. He told the class members to shut their eyes and bow their heads and ask God for candy. When they finished praying, they opened their eyes, but there was no candy. He then instructed them to bow their heads and shut their eyes and ask the communist government for candy. As the children prayed, Viet Cong soldiers placed candy on each desk. When the prayers were completed, the teacher asked the students to open their eyes. Behold, there was the candy! This experiment, he told them, proved clearly who was more powerful, the Christian God or the Communist government.

No, the village problem was far from simple.

When the four men returned to their outfit and gave their report, the platoon got under way in short order and soon reached the first village.

It was searched quickly and no Viet Cong were found. The medic set up shop on the front porch of one of the stores and sent out word for all those who were sick to come by. A long line formed. The medic was not a doctor, but he helped the best he could. He gave shots, pills, and treated sores.

Other soldiers sat around and played with the children. This was where the American soldiers were at their very best. The youngsters shouted with laughter—it was a happy time.

A message had been sent back to the rest of the company and it was now on its way to join the first platoon and then continue through the villages. Soon the entire unit was on its way.

At the next village the same pattern was followed. As the men walked slowly between the huts, they found it completely deserted. Every second they expected a burst of machine gun fire or the boom of an exploding mine, but there was nothing but silence.

After the whole village had been searched and every hut checked out, not a single man, woman, or child had been found. Finally, the Vietnamese interpreter was directed to speak over a portable public address system and tell the villagers that if they came out they would not be harmed in any way but would be given food and medical help.

At this heads appeared from everywhere. Men and women crawled from the many tunnels and edged cautiously nearer. All of them were old, but many brought very young children in their arms. The children were a pitiful sight. They whimpered from the pangs of hunger, and their faces were pale from long days hiding in the dark tunnels. Running sores covered their bodies; their skin was filthy. Only the very young and the very old were left in the village. As the soldiers walked toward them, their bodies trembled with fear.

"Ask them where the rest of the people are," Captain Brakowski instructed the interpreter.

After some talk the interpreter answered, "Sir, they say that the Viet Cong took them all to the mountains to dig tunnels. They also took all the food from the village and warned the old people they would be back in the future for more food."

"Tell them not to be afraid," the officer continued. "We will do them no harm. We're their friends and have come to help."

When the elderly Vietnamese heard this, they bowed before the captain. Then they spoke to the interpreter, who translated. "Sir, they were told by the Viet Cong that the Americans would eat them. They are much afraid."

Captain Brakowski put his hand on the shoulder of the village leader and said, "Please tell them not to be afraid. Americans never eat people. Tell them that we have a doctor with us and that we will offer medical aid to those who need it."

Again long lines formed, this time to see a real doctor. Almost every child was diseased. It was a sad picture to remember.

✿          ✿          ✿          ✿          ✿

"Say, Chaplain, may I speak to you a minute, sir?" a young soldier asked.

"Sure, let's sit here on the porch. What's on your mind?"

"Well, sir, I want to talk to you in confidence about something. What I mean is, if you don't feel that you can do anything about the situation, I wonder if you would be willing to forget who it was that mentioned it?" the trooper asked.

"Whatever we talk about will be in confidence, Burt. Is something wrong?"

"Chaplain, you've probably heard the talk going around that Peavy is AWOL. Sir, Peavy thinks a great deal of you, and I know that you always stand up for the men. I happen to know where Peavy is and that he's not coming back unless somebody goes after him. You see, I know what is on his mind. I came back myself and I'm glad I did. If Peavy could just be brought back, I know he would get things straight in his mind in no time."

"What happened to him, son?" Peavy had always been one of my favorites. I liked all of my men and would have done anything to help any of them, but I felt especially close to Peavy. I knew he was AWOL and was eager to find where he was.

"Chaplain," the soldier continued, and then hesitated, "I don't

know how to say it to you, sir. Peavy went with me to Saigon.
He was sore at Stagg and had loused himself up by not doing
what the sergeant told him. Anyway, Stagg promised to court-
martial him and he was pretty shook up. When we got to Saigon,
we went to the Top Hat Bar, had a few drinks, and Peavy met
a girl. She was one of the hostesses, and he fell for her like a ton
of bricks. Sir, I know you realize how things like this go. When
it came time to leave, Peavy wouldn't go. I told him the girl was
just a hooker' like all the rest and he took a swing at me. I couldn't
do anything with him so I just left by myself. I know he's not
gonna come back, Chaplain, and I'm afraid he's gonna get into
a lot of trouble. I don't know what you can do, but I just thought
that maybe somehow you could help him."

"Where can I locate him, Burt?"

"Chaplain, he hangs around the Top Hat Bar. The girl's name
is Judy. That's about all I know."

"Burt, I appreciate your telling me this. I'll bring him back
if possible, and I won't tell anybody."

"Thank you, sir," Burt replied. "If I can be of any help, just
let me know."

My new assistant, Gus Jenkins, strode over, and looked around
to see if anyone could hear him. "Chaplain," he said, "I got the
word through the grapevine that you're in a little hot water
with your senior chaplain about your trip into Saigon with us.
He wants to see you. That's what his message is about, I think.
I'm sure sorry, Chaplain. If you want me to go in there with
you I will."

"Don't worry, Gus, things always work out."

A loud screaming interrupted us. It turned out to be a little
Vietnamese boy, standing flatfooted on the ground, his fists
clenched, his body erect, and head back. Towering above him
was a young dentist, forceps in hand and a tooth in the forceps.
It was hard to tell who was more frightened, the boy or the
dentist.

Ordinarily the Vietnamese children don't cry when their teeth
are pulled. They cringe as they see the long needles used by the
doctor or the forbidding instruments used by a dentist, but they
are accustomed to pain. Seldom does anyone cry out, but this
one was the exception.

The dentist tapped the little boy on the shoulder; he stopped crying immediately and opened his eyes. Tears rolled down his cheeks. The officer held the tooth out and pointed to the child's mouth. The little fellow's face burst into smiles. He started speaking rapidly in his own language and pointed to his tooth. The other children standing in line behind him laughed and laughed. The dentist put the tooth in the boy's outstretched hand, and he walked away proudly, examining his prized possession. The rest of the children pressed forward eagerly, hoping to be presented with a tooth, also.

"Has anybody seen Lieutenant McNeil around here?" Sergeant Goodman asked as he walked through the area. "If you see him, tell him the Old Man wants him."

"Sarge," a soldier called out, "I know where he might be. About thirty minutes ago he and Specialist-four Hendrickson came by. I heard the lieutenant say they were going over to the west side of the village to check out some bunkers he had heard about. They may still be over there."

"Thanks, I'll tell the Old Man."

When he found Captain Brakowski, he gave him the report. "Damn it, if I told Bull once, I've told him a thousand times not to take off on these wild goose chases without checking with me. How many men did he take with him?"

"Sir, from the information that I have, it was just Lieutenant McNeil and Hendrickson. I don't think they took anybody else."

Captain Brakowski flew into a rage. This was not a common thing for him. Though he was precise, firm, and strictly military all the way, by nature he was a thoroughgoing gentleman. When he got mad, you could be sure there was a reason.

"Well, Sergeant, it figures. Bull McNeil thinks the war can't be won without his personal supervision. One day these chances he takes are going to catch up with him. Get a patrol together and see if you can locate him. He ought to know better than to go out there by himself. I'll bet half this village have family members who are Viet Cong. They ambush us during the day and come right back here to eat and sleep at night. Bring him to see me when you find him."

"Yes, sir."

Sergeant Goodman assembled a patrol, explained the mission to the sergeant he put in charge, and sent it on its way.

The patrol spotted a series of bunkers west of the village, but no life or movement was observed anywhere. The sergeant told his men to check the terrain. In less than a minute the man on the left flank cried out in horror, "Look! Look here!"

It was sickening. The bodies of Lieutenant McNeil and Hendrickson lay inside the first bunker. They were on their backs, and there was no doubt that they were dead. Each had a bullet hole right between the eyes. It was clear they had been shot from very close range. A rusty iron rod was imbedded in each body, and ragged holes indicated where the rods had been thrust time and time again. The bodies were naked and had been mutilated.

The sergeant finally spoke, "Go get some help."

The men just stood there.

"Move out, I said, go get some help. Wait, I'll go with you."

As they left, he directed four soldiers to guard the area and let no one near the bunker.

The word went around like lightning that the lieutenant and Hendrickson were dead. Captain Brakowski was overwhelmed. He and Bull had been very close. I sat with him for a few minutes, neither of us saying a word. When I got up to leave, I laid my hand on his shoulder. "Chaplain," he said, "why couldn't he have just played it safe for once? Now it's all over for him and what was the point of it all?" He shook his head angrily. "Will you do me a favor? Will you please take the two bodies back in and be sure they're taken care of O.K.?"

"Sure, Spence, I'll go in with them. I've got to drop by the senior chaplain's office in Saigon so I'll have to be gone a day or so anyway."

By this time the bodies had been wrapped in ponchos and a helicopter was on its way to pick them up. Word was sent to have the chopper wait for me. As I strapped on my gear, Gus Jenkins reminded me that we had sent out word only a few minutes ago for men to start gathering for a service. He pointed to the good-sized group which had gathered already. In all the excitement, I had completely forgotten.

As I considered the situation, I could hear the chopper motor being revved up. A soldier rushed over to me, and relayed a message that the pilot said to come as quickly as possible because snipers could hit his ship easily this close to the village.

Sergeant Goodman overheard our conversation and suggested that I go on and let him talk to the men.

He continued, "Chaplain, I'm not ordained or anything and am not much of a speaker, but if it's okay with you, I'll lead the men in a hymn, give a brief talk, and then dismiss them with prayer. They'd understand, sir. And then when you get back you can have a regular service."

"O.K., Sergeant, that's a good idea. Go right ahead." Gus and I ran toward the waiting helicopter and took off immediately.

Sergeant Goodman went over to the waiting men. He stood silently before them for a few minutes to get their attention. "Let us begin our service by singing hymn number three on the hymnal card," he began.

As the men in the little congregation looked for the proper hymn, three soldiers walked by, talking loudly and using rough language.

The sergeant yelled, "Knock off that damn noise and profanity! Don't you men know this is a religious service?" He looked at his congregation and said, "Let's have a prayer first."

He prayed.

# Chapter Twelve

# I Cried Like a Baby

Jenkins and I escorted the two bodies to the hospital area, and then went on to the base camp.

"Gus, let's clean up as quickly as we can and get on into Saigon. We can spend the night there and then go to the chaplain's office the first thing in the morning."

"Yes, sir."

"Hello, Chaplain."

We turned around and saw Albright.

"Hi, Alex. I didn't know you were back in. Anything wrong?"

"My leg got infected from some scratches. The doc kept me back in from this operation so we could keep it dry for a few days. We heard you guys had it pretty rough. Sir, I'm sorry to hear about Lieutenant McNeil and Hendrickson."

"Yes, everybody felt pretty bad." After a few moments of conversation, I left to get ready for my trip to Saigon.

Albright said, "Gus, how are the chaplain's plans for the new chapel coming along?"

Jenkins frowned, "Not so good. Two months ago he asked the men to give donations for the new building and wanted volunteers to help build it. He got about enough money that first week to buy the materials. Our men gave quite liberally, but the trouble is, nobody's in base camp long enough to get started. About all we did is pour the cement for the floor and build the frame. I don't know when we'll ever finish it."

"Where does he keep his plans?" Albright asked.

"They stay on his desk most of the time, and all the materials are piled up at the site, but the manpower to put it up is what stops him," Gus explained. "I'd sure like to stay back here, get me a few guys, and put that chapel up for him. Well, I've got to run. See you later, Albright."

In a short while, Gus pulled up to my tent in his jeep and we were on our way to Saigon. We checked into one of the American rest and recreation hotels for the night.

After breakfast the next morning, we drove to the Senior Chaplain's office. Gus and I walked up the stairs toward the reception room.

"Sir, I don't want to butt in, but if you want somebody to stand up for you, I'll sure do it. That Sin-City business was not your fault and you shouldn't have to take all the blame," Gus assured me.

"I'll tell you what, Gus, if they give me five years, I'll see if you can serve two and a half of them for me. O.K.?"

"I'll sure do it, sir, tell 'em I will," Gus replied.

I identified myself to one of the clerks, and asked to see the colonel. I was expected, all right, and in no time at all was ushered into my superior's office. The interview was brief and to the point, and shortly thereafter I walked out again.

Gus was sick with curiosity, but he waited until we got into the jeep to ask, "How did it go, sir?"

"Not bad. He's going to put the reprimand in my records and he ordered me not to reenter Saigon again without his personal permission."

"Oh. Where to now, Chaplain?"

Without blinking an eye, I answered, "To Saigon."

We were silent as we drove toward the heart of the city.

"Sir, where in Saigon?"

"The Top Hat Bar."

"I think I misunderstood you, sir. Where did you say you want to go in Saigon?"

"To the Top Hat Bar."

My answer startled Jenkins, to say the least.

"Chaplain, why in hell, I mean, why in blazes do *you* want to go *there?*"

"Gus, I'm going after Peavy. That's the only contact I have. If I don't find him, he's in serious trouble."

"But, sir," Gus said, *"you're* in trouble already. What's gonna happen if your senior chaplain hears about *this?*"

"I know what can happen if I get caught, but I also know what will happen to Peavy if I don't go after him. He deserves a break. This may be his last chance. I have no choice."

"But, sir, you're disobeying a direct order."

"I'm not altogether disobeying an order, Gus; I'm just disagreeing a little."

"There's no use arguing with a chaplain; I can see that."

"Pull up over there in the parking lot, Gus. I'll walk to the bar."

"Sir, if you're going through with it in spite of everything, at least do me one favor. Let me go to the bar and see if he's there. If he isn't, maybe I can find out where he is. You shouldn't be in there with your chaplain's uniform on."

"Perhaps you're right. I'll wait here. If you don't see Peavy, ask for a girl named Judy. She might be able to help."

Gus walked until he came to the Top Hat Bar. It was early for the regular crowd and only a couple of soldiers and three hostesses were there.

"Hello, soldier," a girl greeted him. "Would you like a drink?"

"Yeah, get yourself one too," Gus answered as he sat down in a booth. The girl got two drinks and sat by him.

"Say, I wonder if you've seen a friend of mine? We're supposed to meet here today," Jenkins said. "His name is Peavy, Shorty Peavy."

"I'm sorry, but I don't know anyone by that name."

"It's very important that I see him today," Gus continued, as he motioned for another drink for the girl. "I brought him some money he wanted. His girl friend Judy works here, maybe they're . . ."

The girl interrupted, "Oh, there is a soldier who is boyfriend of Judy. He comes here often. He may be Peavy."

"Do you know where he is now or where Judy lives?" Gus asked hopefully.

"Are you sure you his friend? You not M.P.?"

"Me an M.P.? What a laugh. Naw, I'm a close friend of his, and I've got to give him this money and get on back to my unit."

"I give you his girl friend's address. He probably there with her." The girl wrote an address on a scrap of paper and gave it to Jenkins. He thanked her, left, and reported back to me.

I decided to take a taxi to the address and let Gus watch the jeep in the parking lot. I didn't want Peavy to know that too many people knew about him.

The taxi driver looked at the address and darted into the traffic. Finally, he turned off the main street into a side road and then went down an alley. After checking the paper again, he stopped at a small house. I paid him and got out.

Hesitantly, I walked toward the door and stood there a few moments wondering what I would say if Peavy wasn't inside. The door was opened by one of the most beautiful girls I have ever seen. Her hair was coal black and hung almost to her waist. And her expressive eyes were as black as her hair.

"Yes?"

"I'm Chaplain Grayson, and I'm looking for someone named Judy."

"I am Judy. Do I know you?"

"No. But I am looking for a friend—your boyfriend, Shorty Peavy."

"Come in," she responded with Oriental grace. "Please sit down. You are a friend of Shorty Peavy?"

"Yes, I'm his chaplain. I've come to talk to him about something very important."

"I think he be in much trouble," she suggested, "and you have come to get him."

"Why do you say that, Judy?"

"Because you are a captain in army. Shorty run away from army, and he said the officers would be looking for him. I cannot tell you where he is. I am very sorry."

I explained that I was a friend and that I had come to help Shorty. Pointing to the cross on my uniform, I explained that I was a man of God.

"I know you tell truth because a man of God cannot lie. Your face has the look of truth about it. I will trust you. Shorty will be here soon. He has gone to the market for me. I am his girl friend. He is number one man, very gentle and honest. His face look much like yours when he speaks." She paused and smiled. "I talk too much. I must learn to listen more as good Oriental girl is taught to do from childhood. Would you like a coke, sir?"

As she left, I looked around. In one corner was an expensive record player and a stack of records. I could not resist taking a look. They were all classical.

"Do you like music?" Judy asked, coming back with the cokes. "I will be happy to play some for you."

As I sipped the coke, I could not help but wonder how Peavy had found a girl like this. In a few moments we heard footsteps on the front porch, the front door swung open, and in walked Shorty.

"Hello, Honey," he said, "I brought the . . ." His eyes met mine. "Chaplain Grayson! What are you doing here?"

"Hello, Shorty. It's good to see you. I've been worried about you."

"Oh, you need not worry about Shorty, Chaplain," Judy interrupted. "He has been living here with me. I take very good care of him."

Peavy's face reddened and he interrupted, "Why did you come here?"

"Shorty, I've come after you. You're too good a guy to be a deserter. I'd like to . . ."

"Chaplain, I'm not going back. There's no use talking. I know you mean well, but I'm just not interested."

"Shorty, you're on a dead end street. It can't last."

"I've found just what I want, and I know what I'm doing. I don't care about the future. I'll take care of that when it gets here. Right now, I'm gonna enjoy the present," Peavy declared.

"Tell me about the present, Shorty. What kind of present is it?"

"Chaplain," Peavy began indignantly, "I'm not gonna hide it and I'm not ashamed of it. Judy and I are living together. I need her and she needs me. We love each other. She's had a hard time of it in the past, and I can make things better for her. I've never had anyone to really love me before, and I intend to keep what we have at any cost."

I attempted to get him to reappraise his situation, to recognize the disastrous results of his decision, and to go back with me and begin again. But it was obvious that Peavy was sold out completely to this new and exciting way of life.

"Chaplain, don't worry about me. I've got plenty of money saved, and when things cool off, I'm gonna get us a flight to the States, get lost, and really live. Or we may decide to stay here. Either way, nobody will ever find us."

Looking directly into Peavy's eyes, I said, "Son, does not getting caught make it all right?"

"I know what you're driving at, Chaplain. But we're gonna get married some day. In the meantime, what difference does a scrap of paper make? We're in love. I know lots of husbands and wives back in the States who have that scrap of paper. Everything's legal, but they hate each other. To my way of thinking, love is what really counts, not the paper."

"You're a religious person, Shorty, is there anyway this affair can square with what you have always believed in?"

In a way, I understood how it was with Peavy. It would be difficult to believe that this dainty, well-mannered, charming girl was anything less than the sweet, next-door-type. Judy was a beautiful girl by any standard. Traditionally, she had been taught the Oriental custom of submitting to the male, and professionally, she had mastered the art of pleasing the customer. American soldiers offered an inexhaustable supply of money, and the only commodity she had to offer was herself. When Judy found a soldier who would provide a steady income, she became a specialist in protecting her investment. To her it was a business, a profession, a livelihood. To a poor boy from the country, timid, starved for affection, it was the love of lifetime.

Shorty answered, "Chaplain, what I believe is my business and how I live is my business. Anyway, the moral code over here is different from that in the States. They look at things different over here. What right do we have in America to think we're right about everything?"

It was obvious that Peavy didn't want any help and couldn't be won by reasoning. But I felt so concerned that I just had to do or say something that would open his eyes. In desperation I blurted out, "Shorty, you know what this girl is, don't you?"

Peavy jumped to his feet. Fury blazed from his eyes. His fists clenched in anger. "Nobody's gonna call my girl a prostitute. Sir, if you weren't a man of God, I'd smash you in the mouth. You'd better leave right now."

My face flushed. I started to speak and reached my hand toward Peavy's shoulder. Peavy stepped back out of reach, interrupting, "Just don't say anything else. I'm sorry if I was out of order, but I know what I want."

I had done the best I could, but it wasn't good enough.

✿        ✿        ✿        ✿        ✿

While Gus and I were in Saigon, the unit out in the field still guarded the same village area, doing the same kind of work day after day. On this particular morning a patrol, led by a lieutenant, was ordered to search a neighboring village. Just as they were about to leave, the first sergeant asked, "Would it be all right if I went along? I'd like to get a look at some of these villages and maybe take a few pictures."

"Sure, Sergeant Goodman," the lieutenant replied. "We're always glad to have the first sergeant with us."

The patrol moved out.

The officer reminded his men, "Don't you guys forget what I've told you. There'll probably be VC's around. Be cautious. We've been alerted about tunnels, so keep your eyes open. Don't go around firing foolishly, but if any VC's jump out, get 'em before they get you."

The men nodded. They might get hit first, but if they did, it wouldn't be because they weren't alert. Every man scanned the area expertly and moved forward to the edge of the village. They passed several tunnels, observing every one carefully. All of a sudden a figure dashed out from the mouth of one of the tunnels. Sergeant Goodman, with the trained reflexes of the soldier, fired instantly. In seconds the rapid fire ceased, and a body lay on the ground.

Sergeant Goodman's mind would not accept what he saw—crumpled in the weeds was a little girl about seven years old. Three shots had torn into her chest, and a small line of blood trickled from the corner of her mouth and worked its way down her chin.

Sergeant Goodman stood there, unbelieving at first, and then visibly broken as the reality of it dawned on him. The color left his face, and his eyes watered. It was painful to watch the inner turmoil and clawing agony which was murdering this man inch by inch. Goodman dropped to his knees by her side, lifted her up gently, and muttered the Vietnamese word for mother. One of the children who had gathered around pointed to the village. The sergeant motioned to them to lead him and they ran on ahead. Soon he stood before the Vietnamese mother, holding her dead child in his arms, a child he had killed himself. He could not understand her words but there was no question as to the meaning of the look in her eyes and of her tears. He could not speak her language, and even if he was able to do so, how could he explain his real feelings? It was obvious that the mother wanted him to leave. She wanted to run to her husband —to cry—to be by herself. But how could he just walk away as though nothing had happened? Goodman could think of nothing to say or do that would express his sorrow. How could he explain that her little girl had just jumped out of the tunnel and that he had fired automatically? How could he make her know that he would gladly give his own life if in so doing, her child could come back to life? It was hopeless. He turned and went away, shoulders sagging.

Word spread rapidly about the death of the little girl. The news was tragic, but the men brushed up against tragedy every day. After all, man can only hurt so much. He soon learns to listen to new reports of death, cringe in his soul, and then go on living.

It was chow time and the men ate as if nothing had happened. But Sergeant Goodman did not eat. He sat on the ground and stared into the distance. If ever a man died while his heart continued to beat, that man was Sergeant Goodman.

Everyone knew what a blow this had been to the sergeant, how he loved children, how he planned after his retirement from the service to give the rest of his life to working with orphans. Actually, the sergeant shouldn't blame himself for the death of the girl. Any other trooper would have done exactly as he did. He just happened to be the one looking at that particular spot at that particular moment when she jumped unexpectedly from the tunnel. No one blamed him, but knowing him, no one was surprised that he blamed himself. He would work this out for himself; it would just take time.

A loud explosion rocked the area. Everyone jumped for cover, and then all was silent.

"Hey, Smith, you and Alonza come on with me and let's check it out." a sergeant yelled.

The three men crawled forward for a short distance, and when no action developed, they stood up and crept forward cautiously.

"Some of you other men fan out and see if you can find out what happened."

"Medic, over here," a voice rang out. "It must be Sergeant Goodman," the soldier gasped, as he turned the body over on its back.

The only way the body could be identified was by the name tag over the shirt pocket. The large black letters spelled out the word, Goodman. But this was all that was left.

No one will ever know exactly what happened. The fragments of an exploded hand grenade were found, and it is certain that this was the cause of his death. It is possible that the pin was pulled accidentally, but not likely. The official report read "Accidental Death."

Though the matter was dropped, it was fairly certain what took place. In all probability the sergeant just walked away from camp, turned his back, took the grenade from his belt, held it close to his chest, and pulled the pin. He could not bear to live, knowing what he had done to the child. Such things are impossible to understand. Perhaps his mind died while he was kneeling by the side of the little girl, and his body was just waiting for a chance to follow.

When I got back to the field, the first thing I heard was about the death of my dear friend and staunch supporter. Stunned and bewildered, I was unable to comment. For the next two days, I could eat nothing—I lay awake all night and avoided conversation.

But I was still the chaplain, as I soon found out.

"Sir, we're supposed to pull out in about an hour for a search and destroy operation," Gus told me. "You think we ought to try to get in a service before we leave? I can call the men together in a few minutes."

I looked at him but didn't answer. It was as though I heard the words but didn't comprehend their meaning.

"Sir, shall I get the men together for a service?"

"No, I don't think so, Gus. We'll line one up after we get back."

The men moved out in about an hour, and Gus and I fell in line with one of the platoons. There was very little talking. The lines moved forward slowly as the going got tougher. The men had to struggle through heavy undergrowth and thorny vines.

An explosion shattered the silence. A Claymore mine had been detonated. Everyone hugged the ground. The force of the explosion tumbled the sergeant through the air and he was unconscious when he hit the ground, but, luckily, the fragments missed him. He would have a headache tomorrow and would be sore for several days, but today, death had refused to accept him.

Gus and I lay side by side. We were at the base of a small

tree and hoped for a degree of cover. Looking at each other, we nodded a quick sign of assurance and buried our heads in our arms.

Machine gun fire opened up. From time to time a bullet whizzed by overhead. And then there was a second explosion. Hot fragments of metal exploded throughout the area. There was a third boom, and then a fourth. They were so near that our bodies heaved with the impact.

Gus grunted. I looked quickly over my left shoulder into the face of my assistant. Jenkin's eyes were closed, but the expression on his face left no doubt about the fact that he had been hit.

"Hold on, Gus, you'll be O.K. Medic, medic, over here."

More machine gun fire opened up, and this time it was more intense than before. I ducked my head and held on.

"Medic, hurry over here," I yelled.

"I'm trying, Chaplain," the medic called out, "but I can't make it yet."

Finally he crawled through the brush into view. There was no sign of a wound on Gus. I had my arm around his shoulder and was softly talking to him. But most of all, I was praying.

"Where is he hit, Chaplain?" the medic asked as he finally reached us.

"I don't know, I can't even see any blood. Maybe in the leg."

The medic ripped open the soldier's shirt. There was no wound. He turned Gus over on his stomach.

"Here it is." There were two small holes just about an inch apart, and a third hole at the base of the skull. Gus had been dead for several minutes.

The cry for medics was coming from every direction now. I looked around and saw men bleeding and grimacing in pain. Snipers were planted in trees above and were firing into the group. Automatic fire seemed to be coming from three locations, whizzing past in a steady stream about two feet above the ground.

Two large jungle rats, frightened by the machine-gun fire, raced frantically away from the noise and toward the soldiers. One man wounded in both legs, became terrified and buried his head as he saw the wild-eyed rats dart toward him. For some reason they turned and avoided contact.

"Withdraw," Captain Brakowski yelled. "Withdraw."

"I'll help, Chaplain," a soldier called as I struggled with Jenkins' body. We carried it to what looked like a fairly safe place, and I went back to help.

The wounded were all being carried to one central area where they could get emergency treatment while they waited for the incoming choppers. The dead were taken to another location. It was a tragic scene—the dead covered the ground. Of the one hundred and sixty men in the company, eighty-five were wounded and fifteen killed.

I walked back over to the body of my assistant, sat down, and cried like a baby.

The choppers touched down in an old cemetery where all the wounded and dead waited. They were loaded hurriedly, and were on their way in record time. Then, all was quiet, and the evening shadows deepened. Orders were to get what sleep we could and continue the search and destroy operation in the morning.

The Viet Cong were somewhere out in the shadows. Would they disappear to avoid our artillery during the night or would they wait until dark and attack? Would they use their own artillery? We wouldn't know until perhaps too late. But the night was peaceful.

The next morning came, and the next, and the next. Each day was the same, "humping it" through the jungle—a mine detonated here and sniper fire there, sweat and mud, leeches and mosquitoes.

But one thing was different—the chaplain. I went out on every patrol and pushed myself without respite. I seldom shaved and was untidy, listless, out of sorts. Something was wrong!

The men noticed that I did not hold any religious services. Most of them figured this was because of sorrow over the deaths of Sergeant Goodman and Gus Jenkins. But those who knew me best realized that this wasn't the whole story.

Captain Brakowski asked if I could talk to him a minute. "Chaplain, how are you feeling these days? You seem to be a little under the weather."

"Oh, I'm O.K. Why do you ask?"

"I don't know, it's just a feeling I have. I kinda sense that something is wrong. Is it?"

"To be honest, Spence, I am depressed, but I didn't know it showed that much."

"You want to talk about it, Chaplain?"

I looked away and didn't answer for several moments while I collected my thoughts. When I spoke, it was with a voice filled with emotion. "Spence, what is there left to say when a minister loses his own faith?"

# Chapter Thirteen

## Angels Come in Black

Back at camp, news spread about Sergeant Goodman and Gus. The men were shocked, especially the old-timers. Albright, who was still not allowed to return to the field while his leg was under medical observation, was especially moved by the report. He had arrived in Viet Nam at about the same time as Goodman and Jenkins and felt a strong tie with them.

Equally as disturbing as the news about the two deaths was the rumor that I was shaken in my faith. Albright just couldn't believe it at first. Though he had always challenged me about Christianity, nevertheless, there was a feeling of closeness between us. It wasn't so much that Albright disagreed with me, as it was that he needed someone to act as a sounding board for his own insecurities. Albright led others to think that he had no faith, that he was sophisticated enough to cast aside infantile religious notions. But deep in his heart he knew that he was drawn to me because I *really* believed. Albright wanted to be won back. And I was the one, he thought, who was strong enough to do it.

Now he was scared. Albright had depended on me to reclaim him, and it was unthinkable that I could doubt also. The thought had never entered his mind that I was human, that I could be hurt, that the weight of disappointment could also crush me.

"My God, did I help do this to him?" he asked himself. "Did I present my arguments so masterfully and press him so often in criticism of his faith, that instead of my receiving answers from him, he received doubt from me? What can I do?" He knew what he had to do. He knew. It came in a flash, "The chaplain needs me; I've got to help him."

From that moment on Albright was alive with the fervor of any old-time evangelist. He set out on a one-man crusade to set things right. The grapevine provided him with the information that I thought I had failed as a minister, that Peavy was in Saigon and not only had refused to return with me but had threatened to hit me, and that my plans to get the chapel built

154

had fallen through. The first project Albright selected was to get the chapel building up. The materials were at the site, but most of the men needed for construction were out in the field. It was a cinch he couldn't count on them, but how could he get the job done without them?

Albright latched onto a plan, unorthodox to be sure, but one that might work. When the troopers had gambled on the outcome of our visit to "Sin City," he was elected to hold the cash. He still had it. The betting had gone sky-high and a great deal of money had come in. In fact, there was more than enough to hire Vietnamese carpenters to put up the chapel.

Albright contacted Jimmy, the Vietnamese businessman. Jimmy got the carpenters. In typical Oriental style, they used ancient tools and worked at a snail's pace. They couldn't and wouldn't be hurried. Finally, Albright decided to pay them on a daily basis and give them a bonus if they finished the job in one week—the day the unit was supposed to return. The work speeded up magically.

When Albright reached into his pocket to get the money with which to pay them the first day, he paused and bowed his head. "Lord, I haven't had many conversations with you. I've been wrong about a lot of stuff, but you know about that, so I don't need to mention it right now. But Lord, this money I'm kind of borrowing, though it wasn't given exactly with church in mind, it sure will help things around here now. So, please, God, just this one time, turn your head and don't look too sharp. I just don't know anything else to do. Amen." Then he paid the carpenters.

His next project was to get Peavy back to the unit. This would take a lot more doing. First, he went directly to the Top Hat Bar and sat down in a booth. When a hostess came over, he said, "Please, tell Judy I'd like to see her."

She shrugged her shoulders and walked through a door in the rear of the room. In a few moments a beautiful girl walked in.

"Are you Judy?"

"Yes, did you ask to see me?"

"I did. Sit down, Judy."

"You knew my name? How did you know me?"

"Oh, I make it my business to know where the really beautiful girls work. I've heard a great deal about you and wanted to

meet you. Since I have to be in the city overnight, I thought
maybe we could take a bottle of champagne to your place and
get to know each other better."

She smiled and answered, "Thank you very much for the invitation but I have plans this evening. Maybe you ask me another
time?" A startled expression crossed her face, and she stood up
quickly and said, "Please excuse me. I must go."

As she left, Albright looked over the back of his booth and
saw Peavy entering the room. He knew then why she had made
her hasty retreat. Peavy might know full well what Judy was
paid to do, but to see her actually sitting in a booth with another
soldier was something else again.

"Hey, buddy, long time no see," Albright called to his fellow
trooper. "Where have you been hiding? Is there room for one
more?"

Peavy was startled, but only for a moment. Both men laughed,
shook hands, and sat down together in the booth.

Peavy explained that he had fallen in love, described his girl,
and then sent word for her to come and meet a friend of his.

When Judy walked in from the back room, she was serene.
She bent down and kissed Peavy on the cheek and spoke to
Albright as though she had never seen him before. She left
shortly with the excuse that she had several things to do.

"What do you think, Albright? She's number one, ain't she?"

"Yeah, she's really something. Say, come on, let's go out and
have a real blast and then get on back to camp."

"I'm not going back," Peavy said. And he meant it.

Albright jeered, "Come on, buddy, don't hand me that. Sure,
you've had your good time with Judy, but these gals come a dime
a dozen. I know you're not sucker enough to take a prostitute
seriously."

Without warning Peavy's fist crashed into Alexander's face.
The blow slammed him back against the booth, and a trickle of
blood ran from his mouth.

"No nigger's gonna call my girl a prostitute. Come on to the
back room and I'll beat your head in," Peavy stormed.

Ordinarily Albright would have taken the challenge, but in the
last few hours he had entered into a process of change. His
personal war was over at last and in its place was a crusade to
help a chaplain find faith. He wiped the blood from his lips and

smiled, "Hold it, buddy, can't you take a little airborne ribbing?"

"Not about Judy I can't. I need some air. I better get out of this joint. See you around." And Peavy left the bar abruptly.

Alexander ordered a coke and asked for Judy. When she saw his lip, she got him a towel and ice. She urged, "You better leave soon. Shorty is much jealous and has number ten temper. Much hot headed. May cause trouble."

"I want to talk to you, Judy. Do you really love Peavy? I want to know."

"Oh, yes, he is my boyfriend now. He give me many things, and we live together at my house."

"Well, Judy, Shorty is heading for real trouble. He left the army, and he'll have to go back. If he doesn't, they'll come after him. He'll be what the army calls a deserter and will be sent to prison for a long time."

"I very sorry. Can you help him?"

"I think I can, but I'll need your help. The only way he'll ever go back is to make him think you're not his girl friend any more. This will be unpleasant, Judy, but we must do it to help Shorty."

"We do this for certain."

So they made a plan. Albright only hoped he could count on Judy. Her expression was troubled and her eyes reflected indecision. She was the key to the whole affair, and he had to be sure she would carry out her part.

"Judy, you've got to help. Shorty can't stay here much longer anyway. I'll have to tell where he is if he doesn't go back. In a few days the military police will pick him up and you'll never see him again."

About five P.M., Peavy returned to the bar and asked for Judy. One of the hostesses said she had gone.

"She left with soldier, the Negro soldier who say he your friend."

Peavy ran out the door and flagged down a taxi. When the cab stopped in front of Judy's house, he paid the driver, leaped out, bounded across the porch, and threw open the door. Albright and Judy were cuddled side by side on the couch in an affectionate embrace.

Peavy went wild.

"Now, calm yourself, boy," Alexander said. "You know what her business is, and my money is as good as yours."

Peavy's reply was to slap Judy to the floor. She lay there, stunned and surprised.

"You're nothing, just trash. All I was to you is money, just a big, fat, ignorant "greenback," and I do mean green. Get into your slop-pen. You're just a pig. I don't want you no more."

He turned to Albright, "And you, nigger, the next time I see you I'm gonna kill you right on the spot. Just don't forget it. Now go on back to her if you want to. You're two of a kind."

He whirled around and rushed out the door.

Albright walked over to Judy and helped her up. Her eyes were full of tears. He felt like a heel.

"Well, our plan worked. It worked just like we thought it would." His words seemed out of place. He continued, "I'd better be going, Judy."

"Albright, please come back one moment."

He turned and waited. "Please one day when far from here tell Shorty that he not number ten and that I not bad girl like he think." She began to cry. It was finished, and there was nothing left to say.

When Albright got back to base camp, he went directly to the site of the chapel. The carpenters would be finished in a few days if they kept at it. The bonus really put a new zip into their saws and hammers.

And now, Albright had to get out to the field to start project three. He had the chapel going up; if he knew human nature, Peavy would throw a drunk and then report back for duty—now for the chaplain. He had no idea what he would say, but maybe somehow all of these things together would put the picture back together again.

Alex hopped the first chopper going out to the field and reported in. Captain Brakowski asked, "Albright, is that leg cleared up?"

"Yes, sir, it's good as new and I'm ready for action. I'm kinda tired of just sitting around."

"We'll see what we can do about that."

The unit was now on what was called the "Silver City" operation. It had been flown by chopper to its new location. Word had been received that a VC headquarters outfit was located nearby, along with some hospital sites. The unit's job was to find and destroy them.

After three days of searching in one direction and then the other, with very little to show for the effort, a good-sized clearing in the jungle was found which was suited perfectly for the incoming supply choppers. The area on the map was referred to as Zulu Zulu and was chosen as the campsite.

The perimeter defense was set up, and everyone "dug in" for the night. Just before it got dark, a series of choppers came and went, bringing in personnel and supplies. Private Peavy jumped from one of the ships, reporting back from being AWOL.

The next morning at 0730 hours an unscheduled helicopter arrived and started its descent. It moved in at about treetop level to choose its exact place of landing. Since the chopper was unexpected, everyone watched. Suddenly, machine gun fire hit it and it burst into flames. The plane went straight down and broke apart.

Fire opened up all around. The Viet Cong were everywhere. Some would run in, heave a grenade, and run back. Snipers in trees picked G.I.'s off with vicious regularity. It was obvious that the unit was surrounded by a large force. Mortar shells began to drop regularly, and the machine gun fire was deadly. To stand up was to die. The battle went on and on and on.

From time to time there was a desperate call for the medic.

"There's one over there," a voice shouted, and rifle fire rang out.

"Help us over here! They're massing on us! Get us some ammunition!"

It was true. The fight had gone on for so long that ammunition was dangerously low. Attempts had been made by choppers to touch down but none could make it. Finally in a desperate effort, a pilot dropped down in spite of the heavy fire. He hovered just above treetop level, and when several rounds thudded into his ship, he abandoned his mission.

"For God's sake, do something," a communications man begged via the 'copter's radio. "We have only a few rounds of ammunition left per man. We've already policed up every spare round we can find. This will be it if something doesn't happen right away."

The chopper made one final run right over the heart of the unit.

"We're gonna drop the crates of ammunition and hope for the best," the pilot yelled into his microphone. "Good luck, you guys!"

Several boxes plunged into the trees and when they hit the ground, the cases smashed open and the contents scattered.

Men ran from all directions toward the ammunition. They scrabbled it up and disappeared into the woods.

One trooper dashed across an open space to deliver a box of ammunition to friends on the perimeter. He was almost there when a sniper cut him in half with a volley of shots.

His best friend, still gathering ammunition himself, saw his buddy go down. He raced across the clearing and the concealed Viet Cong brought him into his rifle sight and squeezed the trigger. Two splotches of blood appeared over the boy's front shirt pocket. The boy staggered and fell face down over the body of his dead friend. He made a slight movement with his right arm, the rifle cracked again, and a circle of blood stained his back. His body slumped and did not move again.

Captain Brakowski kept contact with his men by radio, giving directions and support. He hardly seemed to notice that his shoulder was bleeding. And then, after six hours of torment, all was quiet. Soldiers crawled cautiously from cover. Dead Viet Cong lay everywhere. A final count revealed three hundred and seventy-three bodies. Even though they were the enemy, the sight was still appalling. Many were dressed shabbily and some appeared to be still in their teens.

Fifteen of our wounded huddled under a tree. Everyone was cautious. A new charge could start any time. A sniper could have anyone in his sight who happened to be in the open.

I went from man to man. Some asked for prayer, some smiled and waved, some simply sat silently. One tall soldier was lying on his stomach with the left side of his face against the ground. His eyes were closed. Kneeling at his side, I asked, "Can you hear me, soldier?"

The trooper made no reply and did not open his eyes.

"If you can hear me, I'll have a word of prayer with you."

I prayed and stood up. As I walked away, I looked back. There was a hole in the soldier's skull. He had been dead long before my prayer.

Word came to the command post that some VC were in a bunker located about fifteen meters within the tree line. They had a fifty millimeter machine gun—probably the one that hit the chopper.

For an hour or so an attempt was made to knock it out, but it was so well fortified that not much damage was done. Finally, someone came up with the idea of dropping a small home-made bomb from one of the helicopters. After two or three misses a direct hit was scored. Men crawled slowly toward the bunker until they were able to look down inside.

There was the machine gun and next to it was something no one had expected. A young Vietnamese about fifteen years old, with a steel ring around his neck, was chained to the gun. He never had a chance to escape; his comrades had seen to that.

A few of the Viet Cong were found alive and were questioned for information. One soldier said that two thousand troops had been following the five hundred Americans for several days. At one time, they hid in tunnels and the G.I.'s walked right over them.

The CO decided to stay overnight and send out patrols the next day to see if the VC were attempting to protect something special in the vicinity.

As evening approached, the various lines of defense were set up. No one really expected any more trouble. The VC had been hit hard, but everyone was jumpy, and no one took any chances.

On the outer perimeter Albright sat in a small trench at one of the guard posts. Peavy and another trooper were stationed about ten yards away. It was just getting dark. You could still see, but the shadows had a way of playing tricks.

"Albright!" a voice screamed.

Albright looked around and froze in panic. There was Peavy, his rifle leveled, and pointed straight at him!

"My God, he's gonna kill me! He's found his chance!"

Peavy fired the rifle and the bullet whizzed past Albright's head. There was a gasp of pain and a body fell from a tree and crashed to the ground. No one moved. The sniper had been there all day, undetected, just waiting for a lucky shot. Albright did some heavy thinking. Had Peavy saved his life? Or not? He wondered.

At about ten-thirty that night all hell broke out again. The VC threw in everything they had. War was worse at night. Explosions lighted up the sky, and the noise was unbelievable.

I had rolled out of my hammock into a trench and lay face down in it. These last days had taken their toll. My nerves were ragged, and I began to shake uncontrollably. It wasn't that I was afraid—it was the never-ending anxiety, the sadness and pain that had been compressed into just a few days. I fought to get myself under control, but without success. Finally, I relaxed and lay limp. This helped.

Something fell through the trees and drove into the ground about three feet to my right. It was a VC rifle-grenade. I froze and waited. If it went off, it would be all over. Nothing happened. It was a dud.

Something hit the ground a few feet to my left. It was an enemy handgrenade, but it didn't go off.

I rolled over on my back. Zing! Something thudded into the side of the trench ripping my jacket. Quickly, I explored with my fingers and jerked my hand away. Sticking in the dirt was a hot jagged piece of shrapnel. When it cooled down, I would have a souvenir. Something had missed me three times.

Most of the enemy action stopped. For the rest of the night U.S. artillery shells screeched by overhead exploding just a thousand or so meters beyond.

It was a long night, but morning finally came.

"Hello, Chaplain, how did it go with you last night?"

I looked around and there stood Albright, smiling down at me.

"Well, hello! What are you doing out here?"

"Oh, I don't pass up an opportunity for a good fight, sir. You know me. Say, Chaplain, did you hear Peavy came back?"

"That's the best news I've had this month, Alex. Really great news!"

"Say, Chaplain, when are we going to have a religious service?"

"I'm not sure. I'll let you know if something works out," I replied uneasily.

"That's not good enough, Chaplain. That's just not good enough. I don't want to wait until something works out. I want a service today."

I was startled by this outburst. What was he up to? Was this a cruel jibe at my loss of faith?

Alexander continued, his voice rising in volume, "Come on, Chaplain, I want to hear you say why you are avoiding having a service. Say it to me, sir, so I can understand."

I was dumbfounded. This was the last thing I had expected to hear from Albright.

"Alex, you don't understand. What could I say if I did have a service? I've failed as a minister. What could I offer others if my own faith didn't hold out?"

Alexander interrupted, "Listen, I want to get one thing off my chest. Let's talk man to man. You don't believe we come to you because we think you're perfect, do you? We come because we want to hear what *God* has got to say. Chaplain, you're not God. You're just his messenger boy. We don't expect you to be perfect. In fact, we feel a lot more comfortable around you just knowing that you're human enough to have some doubts."

"But I have failed; I've let you down."

"Chaplain, sir, is this your world or God's? If it's God's, let him have part of the responsibility, and besides, if you quit now, what's going to happen to us?"

I saw tears in his eyes.

"Chaplain Grayson, if you don't care any more, how can we be sure that God does? Chaplain, we need you." With that he got up and walked away. I buried my face in my hands and sat there for a long while. Then I prayed—prayed like I never had before.

The loud voice of the new first sergeant shouted, "All right, we're leaving in thirty minutes. Get set to move out. Police your areas. We're not gonna wait for you, so you'd better be ready." He turned to me and said, "Sir, some of the men are asking about a religious service when we get back. Do you have any definite plans?"

"Yes, Sergeant, pass the word around. We'll be pulling out for base camp in a few minutes and will have a religious service at 1100 hours. There will be a service."

Shortly, we were in the air, and upon our arrival, we were loaded on trucks and on our way back to base camp.

Eventually we pulled into camp with a screech of brakes and a swirl of gravel. I gathered up my gear and climbed out. Instead of being in front of my tent, I found myself staring in disbelief at a *new chapel!*

When the men arrived back in base camp, the first sight that greeted them was the new chapel. It was modern in design but simple in construction—an "A-frame," with a French tile roof and stained glass mounted at each end. Inside were simple pews and a concrete floor. The pulpit stood on one side and the lectern on the other, and in the center was an altar, surrounded by a large kneeling rail.

Just as I finished a quick shower, the doctor called me to his tent to look me over. He kept me right up to the time for the service to begin. Realizing I was late, I ran to the chapel, but as I walked in, Captain Brakowski asked me to please be seated and indicated that one of the men would open the service.

Peavy opened the back door and a group of Vietnamese children filed onto the platform. When they were in place, he said, "This morning we have with us the newly formed 'Sergeant Goodman Orphanage' which our unit has just agreed to sponsor. The children will sing two numbers which Sergeant Goodman taught them himself: 'Onward Christian Soldiers' and 'God Bless America.' "

Peavy sat down and the children sang. There were few dry eyes in the bulging congregation of tough and battle-scarred troopers.

I managed to preach a brief sermon, and before the benediction, I told the men that after the service those who wanted to stay for prayer around the altar could do so. A number of men stayed. As some left the rail, others moved in to take their places. No one seemed eager to go. After a long time only four men were left, Albright, Peavy, Brakowski, and myself. We looked up at about the same moment and recognized each other.

As we got to our feet, Albright said, "I guess I'm the only guy who ever had to go all the way to hell to find God."

Peavy chimed in, "I guess I'm the only guy who ever threatened to punch the chaplain and ended up praying with him."

"Well, that's nothing. I guess I'm the only Company Commander who's proud to have a reformed atheist, an AWOL, and a bar-going chaplain as his three best friends," Captain Brakowski added.

"And I guess I'm the only chaplain who ever had to lose his faith in order to find it."

As we started to go our separate ways, a newly arrived recruit ran over.

"Sir, may I talk to you?"

"Sure, what's on your mind?"

"Sir, they tell me I'm your new assistant. I'd like to ask for a transfer, sir."

"What's wrong? Don't you like the job?"

"Sir, no disrespect to you, but I don't want to hang around in the rear with the chaplain. I want to get out where the action is."